S0-EST-465

THE OXY-ACETYLENE WELDOR'S HANDBOOK

by T. B. Jefferson

SEVENTH EDITION • 1972

a complete, practical manual for gas welding and cutting practice

MONTICELLO BOOKS

MONTICELLO BOOKS, INC.
Morton Grove, Illinois 60053

Copyright, 1929 by the
Acetylene Journal Publishing Company

Copyright, 1939, 1944 by
The Welding Engineer Publishing Co.

Copyright 1948
McGraw-Hill Publishing Co., Inc.

Copyright 1955, 1960 by
Welding Engineer Publications, Inc.

Copyright, 1972
Monticello Books, Inc.

1st Printing

Library of Congress Card Number 72-10143

Printed in U. S. A.

PREFACE

It has been over seventy years since the idea of joining and severing metals with the oxyacetylene flame became a working concept. As gas welding and oxygen cutting grew in popularity, man found a valuable metalworking aid, one that has contributed greatly to the betterment of our way of life.

As other welding processes came into use, some predicted that oxyacetylene welding would fall into disuse. To the contrary, the oxyacetylene flame with its many uses has become more important than ever. Even where other welding processes are involved, the cutting flame has proved to be most helpful in the preparation for welding.

For the sixth time this volume is being revised. Three new chapters have been added and several others have either been completely rewritten or extensively revised. One of the new chapters is one devoted to safety. Welding can be done safely if certain basic rules are followed, and now that the Occupational Health and Safety Act has come into being there is added emphasis on the importance of safe practice in welding and cutting operations. In this added chapter, the reader is provided with safety checks and other pertinent data designed to make him more safety conscious.

Because of our increased leisure time, many people are finding that welding can be an enjoyable "after work" pursuit. Thus, we have added a chapter on the sculptor weldor. Oxyacetylene welding and cutting afford an excellent outlet for the development of new and useful skills for the craftsman. The design and construction of welded scupture can be a rewarding and profitably hobby; for some, the hobby has blossomed into a lucrative vocation.

In the writing and revising of a book of this nature, the author has received help from many sources, and for this assistance he is grateful. There are some people and organizations who deserve special recognition. Among these are: the Rego Division, Golanda Corp., for many of the photos throughout the volume; Mr. Frank T. Kawamoto of the Smith Welding Equipment Div., Tescom Corp., for the pictures of his works in the chapter on the sculptor weldor; Mr. Maxwell Chayat and Airco, Inc., Chemetron Industrial Gases division, and the Eutectic Corporation for their photos and help. I am also indebted to my son, Donald T. Jefferson, who helped greatly in the editorial work in the preparation of this revision, and also made the drawings for the new chapters.

T. B. Jefferson

September 22, 1972

CONTENTS

Preface to Seventh Edition III
Introduction VII
Chapter 1/**THE WORLD OF WELDING** 1
Chapter 2/**THE WELDING GASES** 10
Chapter 3/**WELDING EQUIPMENT** 26
Chapter 4/**SETTING UP YOUR EQUIPMENT** 50
Chapter 5/**METHODS OF WELDING**..................... 71
Chapter 6/**PREPARATION FOR WELDING** 86
Chapter 7/**INSPECTING THE WELD** 114
Chapter 8/**LEARNING TO WELD** 130
Chapter 9/**WELDING PROPERTIES OF COMMON METALS** 140
Chapter 10/**TESTING WELDS** 193
Chapter 11/**IMPORTANT APPLICATIONS** 210
Chapter 12/**OXYGEN-FUEL GAS CUTTING** 234
Chapter 13/**WELDING FOR FUN** 260
Chapter 14/**THE SCULPTOR WELDOR** 275
Chapter 15/**WELDING SAFETY** 299
Index 307

INTRODUCTION

The person who has decided to master oxyacetylene welding, and perhaps make it his life work, is entering one of the most interesting fields of endeavor open to the mechanically inclined. The challenge presented by the problems encountered in welding will require ingenuity; yet, a successful solution is not confined to mechanical methods alone. Almost every application will require thoughtful study.

The field for oxyacetylene welding is as wide and varied as industry itself. The oxyacetylene process is a evolving tool, a field in which advances are continually being made which require alert study by the ambitious weldor. The career—and profit— possibilities are exciting, so long as one uses ingenuity and is willing to perfect the skills necessary in this process.

While there are many exact requirements for oxyacetylene welding, it is not a difficult process to master. The first essential, however, is the thorough knowledge and understanding of the fundamentals. This should begin with familiarization of the equipment employed. Oxy-acetylene apparatus today represents years of design development, so as to produce the ultimate in usable equipment. The various pieces should be studied and their functions understood.

Second is the need to study the correct procedure for every kind of job you might encounter. You must study, also, the characteristics of each metal to become familiar with the best method of joint preparation, the proper flame adjustment, and the specific flux requirements.

Welding can be a vocation or an avocation. Many weldors have made it both — they weld at work and then find enjoyment and relaxation in "after-hours" hobby welding. Under these circumstances, welding can prove to be doubly rewarding.

In our safety-conscious age there are those who have their doubts about combining high pressure gases and "the hottest flame on earth." These, in conjunction, are safe as long as you keep everything under control. Like all we do, welding is as dangerous or as safe as you, the weldor, make it. By learning the proper procedures, and practicing them, welding can be done with safety.

Finally, as a bit of personal philosophy, do your best on each job you encounter, as though that job was to be an everlasting monument to your ability as a weldor. Anyone working under this principle cannot help but succeed.

WORLD OF WELDING

Chicago's 50-ft. high Picasso sculpture was flame cut into desired shapes, and then erected with other welding methods.

CHAPTER 1

THE WORLD OF WELDING

Everyone has some concept of welding or flame cutting. It may be the helmeted worker high on a building framework, crouched over the blinding radiation of his work. It could be the diver bathed in the eerie underwater twilight, cutting through the hull of a sunken ship. Or it could be the skillful body shop weldor at the local garage, replacing a damaged fender with a new raw metal unit, matching the parts as closely as did the car manufacturer.

Whatever his concept, it is safe to say that the layman's perspective of welding is narrow. The man on the street is not aware of the exotic processes which have invaded welding during the past decade or so; electron beam welding, plasma welding, laser-beam welding or friction welding, to name a few. As an evolving science welding is almost continually finding new areas of application, and extensive research by some of America's largest corporations is uncovering and developing newer processes regularly.

Likewise, the layman is not aware of the extent that welding is used today. For example, did you know that your car may have up to 4,000 welds, and that if welding was not employed the vehicle would cost many times as much and yet be an inferior product? Any giant metallic structure build by man can be welded, and many of them

Fig. 1—Modern automatic gas cutting equipment can follow a paper pattern with an electronic sensor, duplicating the desired piece with a multiple head cutting unit.

are: bridges, buildings, ships, planes are examples of products frequently welded. But welding finds its most widespread application in the multitude of items used at home or in business. Appliances, metal furniture, children's toys, tools, and hundreds of other things are made stronger, more attractively and generally more economically through the use of welding.

Welding by the oxy-acetylene process consists of raising adjoining portions of two metals to their melting temperatures, by means of a flame produced by burning acetylene gas in an atmosphere of practically pure oxygen. Such heating causes the selected areas of these metals to flow together and fuse as a homogenous, solid mass.

A great deal of scientific history has been written in which a number of interesting discoveries are shown to have worked together to give to industry the constituents of the oxy-acetylene flame. Acetylene, for example, was known long before it was used commercially. The discovery of economical methods of producing carbide and large scale production of oxygen at rather low cost came very close together. These discoveries were quickly followed by the invention of equipment to utilize these gases in the production of a flame of higher temperature than had ever been known before. It is the perfecting of all these things which has made possible the modern use of oxy-acetylene welding.

It's a vast field, and so we are going to start off relatively simply with the oxyacetylene welding process, which capitalizes on the intense heat obtained in the burning of a mixture of acetylene and oxygen gases under controlled conditions. Properly understood and used, it can join a variety of metals for a variety of purposes, and, by altering the mixture slightly, may be used to cut through a variety of metals.

4 WORLD OF WELDING

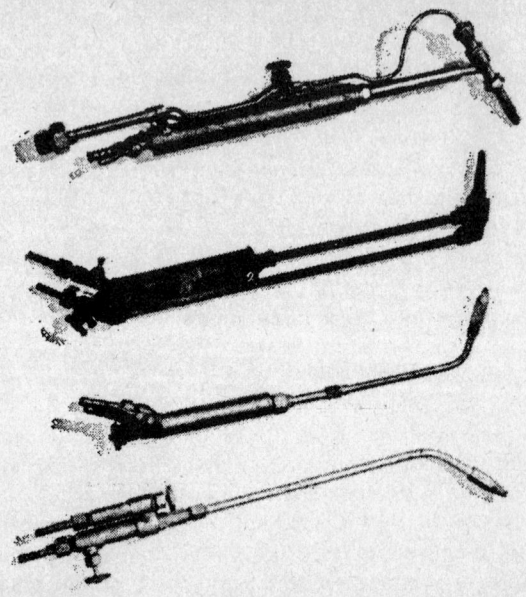

Fig. 2—Although these torches handle different jobs, note the differences between early welding and cutting units above, which measure 18"-20" long, and the new hand size torch below.

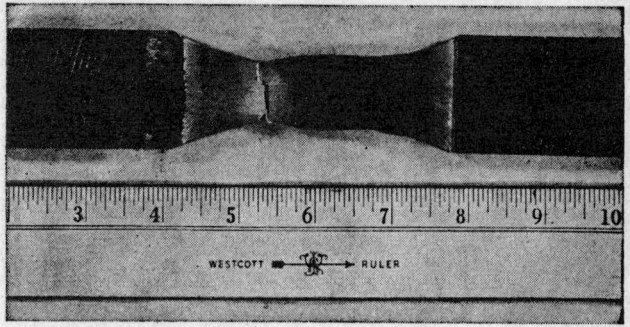

Fig. 3—The properly-made weld (at the 6" mark) is stronger than the base metal, as shown in this tensile test specimen.

The wonder is that by proper use of this technique, two or more pieces of metal can be joined to form a single piece as strong as each of its components. The actual welded joint can be as strong or stronger than the pieces that it connects. With an understanding of metallurgy and proper treatment of the weld zone, a weld can be more abrasion resistant or impact resistant or ductile or have a higher tensile strength than the materials it joins.

The scope of this book permits only a brief historical treatment. Neither is it possible to discuss in detail the value of acetylene gas for other purposes, although a generous share of the world consumption of carbide is in the production of plastics. At one time, acetylene was extensively used for lighting purposes, varying from tiny miners' lamps to lighthouses and marine beacons. The reader who searches the literature of the acetylene industry will find many wonderful and unexpected possibilities in this gas.

BEGINNINGS OF WELDING

The modern art of oxyacetylene welding is only about 75 years old. To give you a little background in this process here is a short history of oxyacetylene welding.

The foundation for the oxy-acetylene welding process, as we today know it, probably lies with a scientific paper presented in 1895 by the French chemist, Henri Louis Le Chatelier. LeChatelier discovered that the combustion of equal volumes of oxygen and acetylene produced a flame

Fig. 4—The first big pipe welding job involved a water line in the Colorado mountains during the winter of 1911.

Photo—Courtesy, Airco.

having a temperature far higher than any other gas flame previously known. In his papers he also noted the non-oxidizing character of this flame.

In the same year, Dr. Carl von Linde began operating a liquid air production plant in Germany, the forerunner process to the present method of extracting oxygen from the atmosphere for commercial use. It fell to others to combine these two developments for use in joining metals.

The first to succeed was Edmond Fouche. In 1900, as

general manager of a firm which used both compressed acetylene disolved in acetone and oxygen under pressure, he utilized these pressure to get the proper mixture. Further refinements were necessary to permit the system to operate on acetylene supplied directly from an acetylene generator at normal pressure. However, by 1903 the oxyacetylene welding process was being used industrially in Europe, and the stage was set for its exportation to the United States.

Oxy-acetylene cutting was first demonstrated by Thomas Fletcher of England in the late 1880's. One leading safe manufacturer was more distressed than impressed by this demonstration, protesting that "this process can only be used for felonious purposes, and has to be surpressed." Sure enough, shortly after its commercial introduction in 1901, "safecrackers" were among the first to put it to use.

Safecrackers still use the oxyacetylene process from time to time, but there has been vast strides in refinement of oxyacetylene welding during the 20th century. The equipment has gone through an evolution of design, and today is modern, light weight and safe. Torches are balanced to minimize the operator fatigue; apparatus is more accurate and reliable, and few areas of the country do not have a welding supply distributorship close at hand where equipment and gases may be obtained.

TERMINOLOGY

The terms "gas welding," "fusion welding," and "torch welding" are all in more or less common use today. In this volume we will restrict our use to either "gas welding" or "oxy-acetylene welding;" the latter, of course, is the more accurate term.

To avoid confusion, the term "Oxy-acetylene welding" should be restricted to welding operations performed with a welding torch which uses acetylene as the fuel gas. Other gases are finding increasing use for brazing activities — most notably, propane and MAPP — but acetylene is the only fuel gas which can be used for welding.

An additional reminder may be useful at this point. Our definition of the oxy-acetylene process indicates that a weld is produced by a combination of metals and heat. Good welding, therefore, is the result of an adequate knowledge of both, and the proper control of each factor in this combination.

The experience gained by practice is the best means of mastering this control. A set of instructions, such as found in this book, can serve to shorten the duration of this skill-developing process, by pointing out ways to avoid mistakes frequently made by others.

The reader will also notice the term "weldor," and the "or" ending may be somewhat confusing to him. The author, some years ago, originated this term to differentiate from the "welder," which is the term also applied to arc welding machines. With two terms, one could stand for the man, and the other for the machine. While "welding operator" or "welder" are still used by some authorities, acceptance of the term "weldor" is growing because it eliminates the confusion.

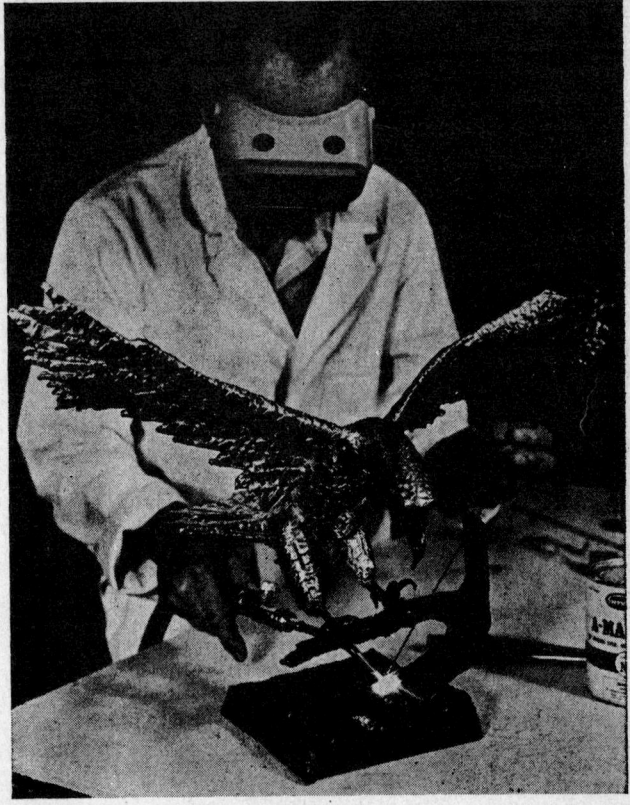

Sculptor Frank Kawamoto putting finishing touches on his handsome landing eagle.

CHAPTER 2

THE WELDING GASES

OXYGEN

Oxygen, a colorless and odorless gas, is the most abundant element on the earth. It is, however, never found in a free state, but is always combined with other elements.

In the gaseous form, when combined with nitrogen, hydrogen, etc., we breathe it as air. It is a major constituent of the atmosphere. Another excellent source of oxygen is water, which contains 89 percent oxygen by weight and 33 percent oxygen by measure. There are a great many oxides present in nature, which, of course, contain a certain amount of oxygen and, in some instances, provide a source of oxygen. Oxygen is best known for the fact that it supports combustion. It is the oxygen in the atmosphere that accounts for combustion. If flames are shielded from a supply of fresh air, they would soon die out.

This gas has a slightly higher specific gravity than air. The boiling point is −296.5 F. In liquid form at this temperature it has a faint blue color, but the liquefied gas is very clear.

Producing pure oxygen

The development of methods for producing oxygen on a very large scale at low cost paved the way for the development of the oxy-acetylene process. Because acetylene is practically an ideal fuel gas, it is natural to assume that the combustion of such a gas in pure oxygen would produce the highest flame temperature obtainable. This, in fact, is the case.

Since oxygen does not exist by itself in a pure state, it is obtainable only by separation—from the atmosphere or water. There are a number of chemical processes which make it possible to obtain free oxygen from such substances as barium dioxide and sodium peroxide, but in practice such methods have gradually been displaced by the more economical processes by which oxygen is obtained from either air or water.

Oxygen is readily obtained from water by electrolysis. This process separates water into oxygen and hydrogen. The oxygen produced in this way is often referred to as electrolytic oxygen. There are still a few plants engaged in the manufacture of the gas by this process.

Air liquefaction

A process more extensively used for the manufacture of oxygen is known as the air liquefaction process for obtaining oxygen from the air, and producing what is commonly referred to as liquid air oxygen. This process consists of reducing air to a liquid, then allowing the temperature to rise to the point where the nitrogen present in the air will evaporate and leave oxygen in liquid form. The liquid oxygen is then drawn off into cylinders for shipment.

It is interesting to note that both processes of producing oxygen utilize a raw material which represents practically no cost, and that both produce gas of much higher purity than can be obtained by any of the other chemical methods. Therefore, the most economical methods are also the most satisfactory, as far as the quality of the product is concerned. The two processes have been developed to a point which allows the production of oxygen on a large scale, with less than ½ of 1% impurities. The high quality of the oxygen gas manufactured in the United States is the result of extensive research work which has characterized all manufacturing processes in the oxy-acetylene industry. Research work has also been of great value in helping users to get superior results from the process.

Oxygen in Cylinders

Oxygen of the ordinary commercial purity is not explosive and consequently is perfectly safe to handle in a properly constructed container. Since it is compressible, this gas is sold compressed in steel cylinders. These cylinders carry oxygen compressed from 1,800 to 2,300 pounds per square inch (psi), and the standard sizes contain from 60 to 300 cubic feet of oxygen when they are fully charged. Oxygen cylinders are necessarily fabricated in accordance with specifications prepared by the Interstate Commerce Commission and since these specifications are designed to allow the transportation of compressed gas with perfect safety, it can be assumed that an oxygen cylinder is a perfectly safe piece of equipment so long as the user observes the common-sense safety rules which have been suggested covering their use.

Safety rules

The first and most important safety rule in handling oxygen cylinders is to use no oil. This means to allow *no oil or grease of any kind* to come in contact with the valve, regulator or any other portion of the cylinder. It means to avoid handling cylinders, particularly the valves, with greasy hands or with greasy gloves. Under no circumstances should valves or regulators on oxygen cylinders be lubricated with oily substances. The reason for this is the great affinity which oxygen has for oily substances; the combination of oxygen and oil results in explosive spontaneous combustion.

When oxygen under pressure is brought in contact with oils or oily substances at the right temperature, the oxidizing process will take place so rapidly as to take the form of an explosion. Since oxygen in cylinders is under high pressure, it is vitally essential to keep all forms of oil away in order to avoid producing an explosion.

Oxygen combines with iron when the latter is left in the open air, forming an iron oxide commonly known as rust. This is a slow process. However, when wood is raised to the proper temperature, the oxygen of the air will combine with it and do this so rapidly as to produce a flame. Burning of any kind is a rapid oxidizing process. Iron itself can be burned when raised to the right temperature and supplied with a blast of pure oxygen under pressure. This is also a rapid process.

Cylinder storage

It should also be remembered that most gases expand when the temperature is raised, and that the usual procedure in filling oxygen tanks is to allow a certain maximum pressure at ordinary room temperature. Therefore, it is advisable to store full cylinders in places where they will not be exposed to the heat of stoves, radiators, furnaces or to the direct rays of the sun. In order to guard against accidents, in case this caution is not observed, oxygen cylinder valves are provided with safety plugs or discs which either melt or blow out if the temperature is raised above the safety point. The user is thereby protected from bodily harm, but the blowing of the safety plug means the loss of the entire contents of the cylinder.

It is advisable to store all full cylinders not in use in one place where they cannot be tampered with by unauthorized persons. They should also be well separated from such things as carbide containers, acetylene or other fuel gas cylinders and acetylene generators.

In the storage room where full oxygen cylinders are kept, open flames (cigarettes included) should be prohibited because any escape of gas might greatly increase the volume of such flames. In general, it is advisable to provide storage space well removed from combustible materials, keeping in mind that oxygen itself does not burn, but it supports combustion.

Empty cylinders should also be assigned a definite storage area, and should not be allowed to accumulate longer than is absolutely necessary from a practical standpoint. Considerable savings can result from the prompt collection and return of empty cylinders, with particular attention given to separating the oxygen cylinders from the fuel gas cylinders except when actually in use.

Care in handling

It is advisable to exercise reasonable care in handling oxygen cylinders. If a crane or derrick is used, the cylinders should be placed in a suitable container to insure against any possibility of their dropping. When actually in use, it is advisable to have them rigidly supported so that they will not be easily knocked over. (Fig. 1) Under no circumstances should they be used as rollers or as supports for equipment or metals.

It is a good practice to have a small hand truck available for transporting cylinders from the storage point to the point of use, and to make sure that the valves are closed while the cylinders are being moved. Safety dictates that cylinder valves should be closed whenever work is finished, a cylinder has been emptied or a cylinder is returned. Every cylinder carries marks and numbers of the oxygen manufacturer who filled it; these

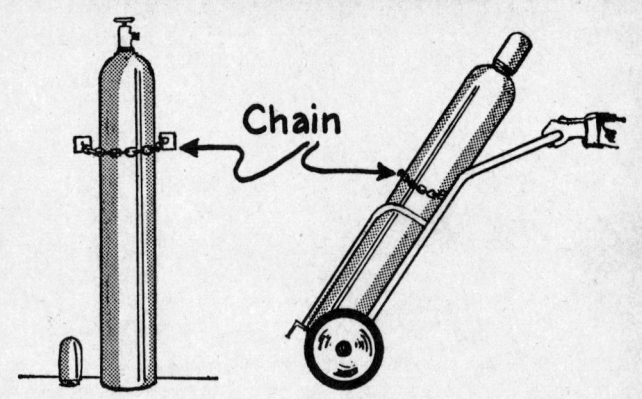

Fig. 1—Safe practice minimizes the danger of toppling.

marks should not be changed or defaced in any way by the user. To do so is illegal.

Estimating amount used

It is not difficult to obtain a very close estimate of the amount of oxygen used in a given job, provided the capacity of the cylinder and the initial pressure in the cylinder are known. If for example a 220 cu. ft. cylinder shows a pressure of 2000 psi, (at room temperature of 70° F) each cubic foot of gas consumed would cause the pressure to drop 10 psi. In other words, a pressure drop of 100 psi on the high pressure gauge of the regulator would indicate that 10 cu. ft. of gas have been used. It is good practice to become accustomed to figuring the gas consumption in this way so as to be able to know approximately how much gas will be required for a given job and provide enough gas in each case to carry the job through to completion.

Oxygen Manifolds

Large scale oxy-acetylene welding and cutting operations often involve the use of oxygen in such quantity that the use of single cylinders by each operator is not economical. In such cases it is quite common to connect a number of oxygen cylinders to a manifold and supply oxygen through pipe lines to stations where it is used. The advantage of this procedure is less handling of cylinders; it is also possible to keep a careful check on gas pressure used by individual workmen. However, the installation of manifolds and oxygen pipe lines is subject to regulation and involves engineering problems which are beyond the capacity of the layman. Such installations should, therefore, be made only by experienced engineers who are familiar with the problems of manifold installations and the regulations covering the supply of oxygen through pipe lines.

The Safe Use of Oxygen

Some poorly informed workmen have an impression that oxygen is only highly purified air; in fact, in some plants it is commonly referred to as "air." This is an unfortunate and dangerous practice, with disastrous results. Oxygen should never be used as a substitute for compressed air when blowing out pipe lines, operating compressed-air-oil burners or air tools, testing tanks, starting engines, etc.

Likewise, oxygen should never be transferred from the cylinder in which it is supplied by the manufacturer into any other kind of container, nor should the contents of a full tank be transferred to an empty or partially empty one.

The user should keep in mind at all times that the instructions issued by the manufacturer are common-sense safety rules dictated by knowledge and experience. They are for the benefit of the user and for the protection of life and property; all such instructions should be OBSERVED TO THE LETTER.

ACETYLENE

Acetylene is a hydro-carbon gas which was discovered by Edmund Davy in 1836. It was not, however, until Woehler announced in 1862 that acetylene gas could be produced from calcium carbide that the gas really became known. Even with the announcement the discovery was of little value, since calcium carbide was not produced commercially. However, in 1892, Thomas Willson, of Spray, N. C., in an attempt to produce metallic calcium, discovered a means of producing calcium carbide. Shortly afterward he established facilities to produce carbide commercially, making acetylene gas readily available. It then became recognized as a valuable illuminating gas.

Calcium carbide

Calcium carbide (also called carbide of calcium, or simply, carbide) is a dark gray or bluish black substance, brittle, with a crystalline structure, and technically defined as a chemical compound of carbon and calcium. The compound does not retain the characteristics of either of the elements which it contains. It is manufactured in an electric furnace by fusing together 56 parts of lime (by weight) and 36 parts of coke.

Manufacturing experience has indicated that the use of low quality materials will result in inferior-quality carbide with a low gas yield. The gas thus produced is a low grade of acetylene which must be purified chemically before it is fit for use in welding. For this reason the manufacturers of carbide are particular in the selection of raw materials.

Carbide will last indefinitely if it can be protected from contact with the air or water. It is not combustible by itself and is, therefore, perfectly safe for transportation and storage as long as it is kept in sealed containers.

However, as soon as it is brought into contact with water or any mixture containing water, it decomposes and gives off acetylene gas. If left exposed to the air, it will decompose slowly under the influence of atmospherio moisture. The slight odor of carbide is, indeed, attributed to the small quantity of the gas produced in this way by exposure to the air.

Acetylene production

Acetylene has already been mentioned as a product of the reaction of water and calcium carbide. The chemical equation for this reaotion is:

$$CaC_2 + 2H_2O = C_2H_2 + Ca(OH)_2$$
Calcium   Water   Acety-   Calcium
Carbide   lene   Hydroxide

This reaction is instantaneous. The carbon in the carbide combines with the hydrogen in the water, forming acetylene, a hydro-carbon gas. The calcium combines with oxygen and water, forming calcium carbonate, or lime, which has a great variety of uses, and so may be considered as a by-product of some value. It may be noted as a matter of information that acetylene can be produced by other means, but there is no method of producing it which can compare in practicability and economy with the water and carbide method.

The special value of acetylene to the weldor is its enormous capacity for producing heat when burned in an atmosphere of pure oxygen. The flame temperature produced is authoritatively estimated to range between 5,500° F and 6,300° F. A "neutral" flame, the result of the combustion of equal parts of oxygen and acetylene, yields a temperature of 5,850° F. Excess oxygen may produce a flame temperature of up to 6,300° F. but the oxidizing flame may be very harmful to metals.

OXY-ACETYLENE TEMPERATURES

Ratio of Oxygen to Acetylene	Type of Flame	Temperature
0.8 to 1.0	Carburizing	5550° F
0.9 to 1.0	Carburizing	5700°
1.0 to 1.0	Neutral	5850°
1.5 to 1.0	Oxidizing	6200°
1.8 to 1.0	Oxidizing	6300°
2.0 to 1.0	Oxidizing	6100°
2.5 to 1.0	Oxidizing	6000°

Fortunately, the flame is easy to regulate so as to get greatest value out of the gases. A properly constructed oxy-acetylene torch makes it possible to regulate the flow of both gases, so that the desired temperature is evenly maintained, and there is no excess flow or waste of either oxygen or acetylene.

Safe practices

Now that the value of acetylene as a fuel has been established, the discussion will turn to the consideration of safety; for, like all combustible gases, acetylene has its explosive range. When present in a confined space in a mixture with air or oxygen, it is, of course, explosive at any pressure if a spark or open flame contacts the mixture. When compressed to a pressure in excess of fifteen psi in a space of any appreciable size, it may be caused to explode by shock or jar, or by self-generated heat. It is, therefore, of greatest importance from a safety standpoint to avoid the generation or the accumulation of acetylene in a free state at a pressure in excess of 15 psi.

A few of the qualities of carbide and acetylene can readily be demonstrated by a simple experiment. Place a small piece of carbide on a piece of scrap metal, sprinkle a little water on it and light it with a match. Note that the carbide itself does not burn readily, and that the flame will die out when the water has produced its capacity of acetylene. Sprinkle a little more water on, ignite again, and while it blazes freely sprinkle on more water, noting a big increase in the flame due to increased gas production. Then note that quite a lot of black soot is floating in the air. This is unconsumed carbon, because there is insufficient oxygen in the air, under the conditions, to produce perfect combustion. Keep this little demonstration in mind when reading about the carburizing flame in a subsequent chapter. It will be found that a more complete combustion of the acetylene can be accomplished by utilizing a bunsen burner or by feeding a jet of compressed air to the flame. The most perfect combustion is obtained by means of the oxy-acetylene torch which mixes oxygen and acetylene in the correct proportions.

Types of Acetylene Generators

There are two ways to obtain acetylene for oxy-acetylene welding and cutting. One way is to make it from carbide in a suitable generator; the other is to purchase it in tanks from manufacturers of "dissolved" acetylene.

With reference to the method of making acetylene direct from carbide, this practice was in much wider use in the past than today. With the convenience of distribution centers for compressed gases, the use of acetylene generators is now largely confined to commercial gas manufacturers.

CAUTION: One should not attempt to make his own acetylene generator. The illustration (Fig. 2) of the operation of the carbide-to-water generator is not complete. **It is not suitable in any respect to use as a working drawing for the construction of "home-made" generators.**

OXY-ACETYLENE WELDOR'S HANDBOOK

Acetylene generators are made to operate on several different principles. One of these is the "water-to-carbide" principle. This principle is used in situations where the volume requirements are very small. It is not suitable for generators of the size required for welding because too much heat is generated.

The design of another type of generator is based on the contact principle, in which water comes into contact with carbide within a "gas bell". The gas thus produced is trapped in the bell, to be released as needed.

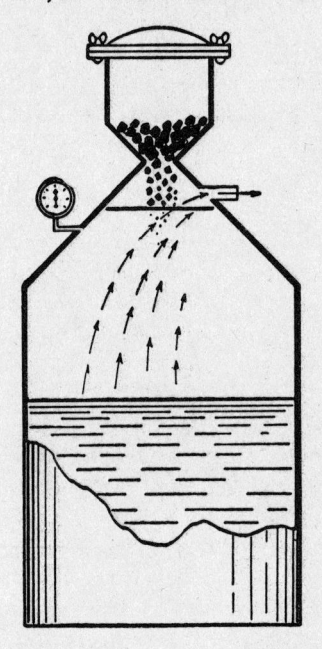

Fig. 2—Working principle of carbide-to-water acetylene generator.

The most widely used type of acetylene generator for welding is constructed on the "carbide-to-water" principle.

It operates by dropping carbide into water, so that acetylene rises to the top and is drawn off through an outlet to the torch. The water compartment of this generator is large enough to hold one gallon of water for each pound of carbide which the hopper will contain. This amount of water is necessary to keep the generator cool during operation until the carbide supply is exhausted.

The choice between buying acetylene cylinders or manufacturing your own gas is not much of a consideration today in the United States, most weldors opt for the cylinder. While the cost of generated acetylene is about 40% less than that purchased in cylinders, other economic considerations (such as the initial cost of installing a plant) and the ready availability of acetylene in cylinders in most locations have diminished the economic consideration.

Today, you are most likely to find acetylene generators only in remote welding locations, where the cost of transporting cylinders would be prohibitive; in scrap yards or large welding shops where a number of weldors or cutters are working continuously in fixed posts and require a continuous supply of gas; or in welding distributorships who manufacture and then compress it into cylinders for sale.

New federal and state safety regulations have also placed limitations on the use of acetylene generators. The location and operation of such generators is carefully controlled, and it is doubtful if any large cities permit operation of these units within their borders. In other areas, the presence of a generator might raise insurance rates to unacceptable levels. Thus, for most welding operations, acetylene in cylinders is the most practical and convenient form for the supply of this gas.

Acetylene in Cylinders

Although the generation of acetylene for direct use is a simple matter, its production in suitable containers for shipment is a specialized manufacturing industry. It is obviously not economical to use containers large enough to carry any considerable volume at such a low pressure as 15 psi. Therefore, acetylene cylinders are filled with a porous substance which is saturated with a liquid solvent (acetone) capable of dissolving many times its own volume in acetylene. Acetylene is forced into the cylinder and is absorbed by the acetone.

Cylinders for welding range in capacity from 10 cu ft to 323 cu ft. Those supplied by reputable concerns can be depended upon to contain ample safety devices. Since they are easily carried about, and each cylinder holds an ample supply of acetylene for the average welding job, the use of acetylene in this form, correctly called "dissolved acetylene," is very popular. The processes of filling acetylene cylinders can be carried on with safety only in plants especially built for this purpose, and then only when the work is supervised by men who are thoroughly familiar with the operation. Special compressing equipment and various kinds of accessory equipment are required.

It is well for the user of tanked, or dissolved acetylene, to bear in mind that he pays for the gas only, and that the container is the property of the gas manufacturer. Furthermore, the same tank or cylinder after being returned will probably be used by some other customer. The owner of the cylinder has the sole right to refill it when it has been emptied of acetylene, and every safety consideration favors the return of cylinders to their proper owners for service of any kind. **Under no circumstances should a user try to fill or partly fill an empty acetylene cylinder from a full one.**

Care of cylinders

Acetylene tanks are readily distinguished from oxygen tanks because they are generally shorter and of larger diameter. Their contents are heavier, so they are also more difficult to overturn. They should be handled with reasonable care and kept upright, both in storage and in use. Particular care should be exercised to protect the valves from damage or abuse.

Since acetone is both valuable and essential to the acetylene cylinder, reasonable precaution should be taken to prevent any loss of this liquid. Empty tanks should always have valves tightly closed. If a tank has been lying on its side and acetone starts to leak out when the valve is opened, it is advisable to set the tank upright again, and leave it for a while so that the solvent may work back into the porous filler.

A dry, well ventilated place for the storage of acetylene cylinders is recommended. Preferably they should also be protected from extreme cold, although this is not considered to be of great importance. The storage space should be remote from other combustible materials and also from stoves, furnaces, or open flames of any kind. Leaks are immediately detected by the unmistakable odor of acetylene, and should be located by using soapsuds on the valves. **Never use a match.** A leaky valve may sometimes be fixed by tightening the gland nut. If this does not work, or if the leak is found to be in a safety plug, do not attempt further repair, but release the acetylene in the open air and return the cylinder plainly marked to show that it is defective. **Never tamper with safety plugs in any way.**

Rate of gas withdrawal

There is a limit to the rate at which acetylene may be withdrawn from a cylinder with good results. If it is drawn out too fast, some of the acetone will come out with detrimental effect on the flame and the weld. It has been estimated that the maximum rate should be one-seventh the capacity of the cylinder hour. In other words, a full cylinder should last for seven hours of continuous welding; a more rapid rate of consumption is not good practice.

It is not possible to determine the contents of an acetylene cylinder by the change in pressure as with an oxygen cylinder, but the amount taken out can be determined by weighing the cylinder before and after using. A loss of weight of one pound indicates the consumption of $14\frac{1}{2}$ cu ft of acetylene.

LIQUIFIED PETROLEUM GAS

Propane and butane, better known as LP or "Bottled" gas, are commonly used for heating and cooking, but they also have come into use for some industrial applications. The oxy-propane flame can be adjusted to produce a temperature of 4600° F, suitable for preheating, soldering and brazing. Using oxy-LP gas cutting tips, the preheating flames can be adjusted to produce temperatures up to 5300° F. For this reason LP gas is preferred by many for *cutting* wrought iron and steel. Note, however, that the oxy-propane flame *cannot* be used for fusion *welding* of either iron or steel. (See Chapters 11 and 12.)

During the past few years, several "new" gases, promoted as acetylene substitutes, have been introduced in the welding field. All of these are synthetic petroleum derivatives and are sold in liquid form similar to propane. They must be vaporized into a gas for use.

Marketed under such brand names as Apachi, Flamex and MAPP, some are said to have the capability of producing a flame of sufficiently high temperature for welding. This is probably true, but the welding activities must be confined to thin gauged materials.

CHAPTER 3

WELDING EQUIPMENT

Before the reader attempts oxy-acetylene welding, he should become familiar with the welding outfit. This includes: an oxygen regulator, with two gauges which read "O to 80 psi" and "0 to 4000 psi" respectively; an acetylene regulator having two gauges, one reading "0 to 30 psi" and one "0 to 500 psi;" and two colored lengths of hose, the green used to transfer oxygen, and the red hose for the acetylene.

The welding torch, which is provided with needle valves for controlling the flow of gases, may be fitted with one of several size tips. In addition, the welding outfit includes a torch lighter, weldor's goggles, regulator and torch wrenches and usually an assortment of flux and welding rods for various welding operations. In some instances, a cutting attachment (which is described in Chapter 12 is also provided with the welding outfit.

PRESSURE REGULATORS

The gas pressure regulator or reducing valve is an indispensable part of the oxy-acetylene welding outfit. Acetylene gas is quite commonly furnished under pressure in steel cylinders, and oxygen is practically always supplied in cylinders under high pressure. These pressures are very much in excess of the pressures which it is possible to use for welding or cutting. Consequently, it is necessary to provide some method of supplying gases to the welding or cutting torch at the desired pressure.

Single-stage Regulators

The device used for pressure regulation, commonly called "a regulator," consists of a mechanism arranged to receive the gas from the cylinder at a high pressure and deliver it at a lower pressure to the hose line leading to the torch. (Fig. 1). Above the regulator body are two gauges. One, called the high pressure gauge, indicates the pressure of the gas in the cylinder. The reading of this high pressure gauge will constantly diminish as the gas is drawn from the cylinder through the torch. The second, the low pressure gauge, indicates the pressure at which the gas is being delivered into the hose line. If everything is functioning properly, this reading will be constant throughout the welding or cutting operation.

It is obvious that if the regulators are in good condition and working properly, it is possible to adjust them so that the volume of each gas delivered to the torch for the maintenance of the flames will be exactly right and will remain in the correct proportion automatically.

Construction

The essential parts of a pressure regulator (Fig. 2) are a gas chamber, a diaphragm, a seat, control spring, operating lever and the two gauges mentioned above. The diaphragm of the regulator forms one wall of the gas chamber and is held in position by a spring controlled by the adjusting screw. The diaphragm is also connected to the gas inlet valve, so that its movement will open or close the gas inlet by joining or separating the opening of the inlet valve at the seat. When the gas chamber is empty, this valve will be open.

WELDING EQUIPMENT

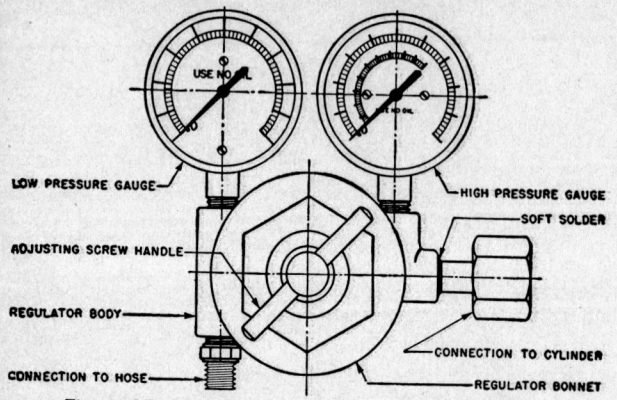

Fig. 1.—Essential parts of pressure reducing regulator.

Operation

The high pressure gas from the cylinder flowing into the gas chamber will gradually fill the latter and build up a pressure against the diaphragm and its controlling spring. The mechanism is so arranged that when the pressure is built up to a point high enough to overcome the tension of the spring, a slight movement of the diaphragm brings the seat against the opening of the inlet valve. This shuts off the gas supply, until the pressure is reduced, by drawing off the gas at the outlet. A reverse movement of the diaphragm immediately separates the seat from the inlet opening and the gas from the cylinder again enters the gas chamber.

The operation of the regulator mechanism is a repetition of this action in a continuous cycle, a breathing motion. It is obvious that the delivery pressure is controlled by the adjusting screw and its tension on the control spring. The low pressure gauge works off the gas chamber and tells the operator at any time just what delivery pressure is being maintained.

It is not necessary to go into a detailed discussion and comparison of various types of pressure regulators, for there is a considerable variation in the construction details of different makes. It is essential, however, to realize that practically all of the regulators made for welding and cutting operate upon the same general principle and are composed essentially of the same parts. Furthermore, it is important to observe that every gas pressure regulator is a high precision instrument. No matter how ruggedly a regulator is constructed, it is built to very accurate dimensions and its proper functioning is dependent upon delicate adjustment. Therefore, it is a piece of apparatus which requires careful handling, and rules for the proper handling and care of regulators should be carefully observed regardless of what type is in use.

The Two-Stage Regulator

Precise adjustment of gas flow and non-freezing characteristics may be obtained from the two-stage regulator, which permits precise gas pressure adjustments within very close limits. This control is of great importance in production work where a flame adjustment, once made, must be maintained without fluctuation. Otherwise, the quantity of production or quality of work is affected.

The two-stage regulator is really two regulators in one, with two separate seats and diaphragm assemblies. The first stage takes the gas at cylinder pressure and reduces it to approximately 200 psi. This stage is generally not adjustable. The second stage is adjustable with a screw to any pressure within the range of the instrument. By eliminating the need for one adjustable stage carrying the full cylinder pressure, very accurate adjustments can be made.

CAUTION: **Always be sure to release the spring tension of the diaphragm by unscrewing the ad-**

justing screw before turning on the gas from the cylinder. **Always be sure that the outlet is open when reducing pressure.**

These two rules are to prevent sudden and violent motion of the diaphragm. The explanation of the operating mechanism already given indicates that while the gas is flowing through the regulator, the diaphragm is

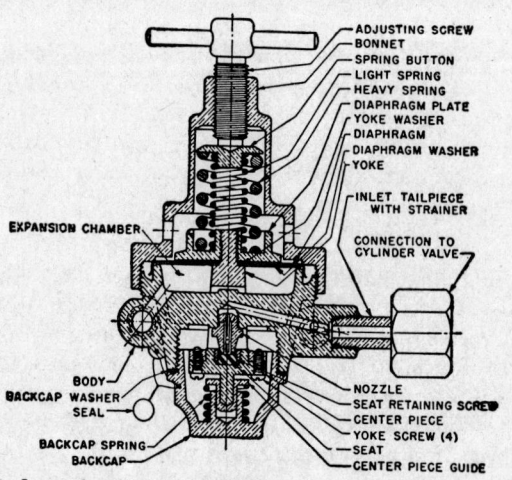

Fig. 2—Internal mechanism of nozzle-type pressure reducing regulator.

constantly in motion and operating to open and close the inlet valve by making contact with the seat. The seat is, therefore, subject to continuous wear and is, in fact, frequently in need of replacement. This wear can be reduced to a minimum and the regulator kept in good condition by preventing sudden, violent action that causes damage to the seat and the rest of the interior mechanism.

Pressure Gauges

An explanation of the working principle of the gauges used on welding regulators will be helpful in suggesting the need for proper care of gauges. (Fig. 3)

Pressure is admitted through a socket into a flexible tube which is held fast at the socket end. (Fig. 3)

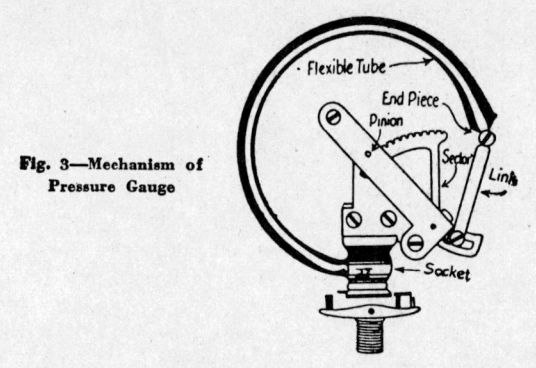

Fig. 3—Mechanism of Pressure Gauge

When gas is admitted under pressure through the tube, the tube tries to straighten out. This movement is transmitted through a double link in a moveable sector, then to a pinion post upon which the gauge hand is mounted. The travel of the hand is governed by adjusting the location of the lower link screw in the slotted sector arm. The tube varies in thickness according to the diameter of the gauge for which it is intended, as well as with the pressure to be recorded. It must be of such proportion so as not to be strained beyond the elastic limit by the application of the maximum average working pressure.

General practice is to calibrate a gauge to double its maximum working pressure. This means that a gauge intended to record a working pressure of 100 psi should be calibrated for 200 psi. Failure to observe this principle causes a gauge to be overstrained and its tube to assume a permanent set. This can be detected by the hand's failure to return to zero when the pressure is released.

High pressure gauges such as oxygen and hydrogen gauges are equipped with safety release features which allow the gas to escape from a ruptured tube while preventing damage to the front glass and dial. In some cases this release comes about by allowing the back of the case to turn back on the hinge; in other cases a brass plate along the side expands and releases the gas.

The following rules are suggested to aid the user in getting the greatest service out of all gauges.

1. Never permit oil to get into any oxygen apparatus. (In fact, keep it out of all oxy-acetylene apparatus at all times.)

2. Never apply pressure to gauges suddenly; rather, try to open the valve on cylinders slowly. Do not apply pressure to the full capacity shown by calibration of the dial. Do not throw on full tank pressures with the regulator's adjusting screw all the way in. Work up the pressure on low pressure gauges slowly.

3. In attaching gauges to apparatus, use a wrench on the square end of the connection.

4. Never throw gauges around or drop them.

5. Do not attempt to repair a defective gauge yourself. Send it back to the factory or to an authorized service station.

6. Do not work with a defective gauge. Have it repaired at once.

7. If there is any doubt about the accuracy of the gauge, it should be tested with a gauge tester, which is a factory or service station job.

If the low pressure gauge builds up pressure quickly when the torch valves are closed and the adjusting screw is released, the fault is probably not with the gauge but with the regular valve seat. This condition is generally referred to as *creeping*. When it is present, the regulator valve seat should receive attention immediately. It is dangerous to continue using a regulator when the gauge it creeping.

As to the regulator itself, there are two parts which may become faulty and need repair. These are the diaphragm and the seat. In some regulators either may be easily replaced by the weldor by following comparatively simple instructions. For more complicated models, replacements may require sending the regulator to the factory.

If the flexible tube inside the gauge is broken or has sprung a leak, the damage will be indicated by improper action and by leakage of gas. A tube which is leaking should not be repaired by the weldor. The entire gauge should be sent to the factory where proper equipment is available for making a complete repair.

A "frozen" regulator indicates that the regulator does not have sufficient capacity for the work being done. When more than the proper amount of gas is released and allowed to expand inside the regulator, a refrigerating action occurs, and the regulator becomes so cold that moisture on the outside is frozen on the body. Inside traces of moisture will become frozen and block up the passages within the regulator. The regulator can be thawed out with hot wet applications but will probably freeze again if again subjected to service beyond its capacity.

New regulators may show a tendency to vibrate or leak. The vibrating can be corrected by adjusting the diaphragm spring or putting in a new diaphragm, while leaking can generally be corrected by a thorough cleaning.

Do not continue to use a regulator which is noticeably defective.

WELDING HOSE

The rubber hose used for carrying the welding gases from the regulators to the torch is quite apt to receive less attention than it deserves. It is important to the outfit because defective hose can cause waste and possibly dangerous working conditions.

A number of manufacturers make hose especially for weldors. Hose so manufactured is known to be reasonably free from accumulation of dust, or "bloom," on the inside, and strong enough to last a reasonable period with the hard service it gets in welding and cutting operations. Therefore, when the hose needs to be replaced, the new lengths should be purchased from the welding equipment dealer who sells hose specifically manufactured for this use.

Replacements can be kept at a minimum by proper care such as: avoiding kinks as much as possible, arranging equipment prior to welding so that trucks will not run over the hose nor heavy objects fall on it, nor will be burned by drops of molten metal. Leaks should be repaired by cutting out a section of hose and inserting a hose union, rather than trying to mend them with tape or any kind of cement. If it is known that a "backfire" has worked back into the hose, the entire hose should be discarded at once before the rest of the equipment becomes clogged up with particles of burned rubber. It is a good procedure to test hose occasionally for leaks because welding gases are fairly expensive and losses from this source are easily eliminated.

THE WELDING TORCH

The oxy-acetylene torch is probably the most interesting part of the welding equipment as far as the operator is concerned. It is the part that he handles constantly while at work. He is naturally interested in its weight, balance, and performance, but should also know just what service it performs in welding.

The function of the torch is to receive the two gases from the cylinders, mix them thoroughly, and deliver a uniform mixture at a steady pressure to the tip for the welding flame. Gases enter the torch through two needle valves at rear of handle (Fig. 4), and pass through tubes to the mixing chamber from which the mixture emerges through a single passage to the tip.

This piece of apparatus must be designed very carefully and made to exacting dimensions in order to insure correct proportioning of the gases. The mixing chamber itself is an intricate device, varying in con-

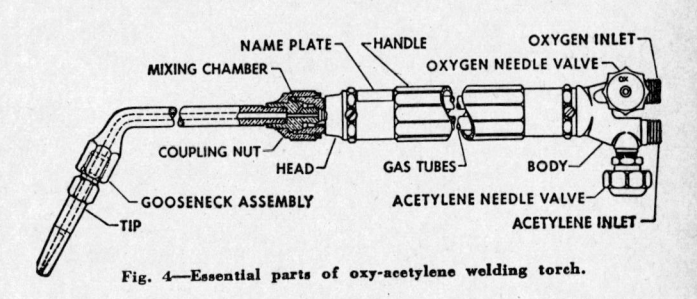

Fig. 4—Essential parts of oxy-acetylene welding torch.

struction and location in different makes. The design must also incorporate some device to prevent "flashbacks," (which will be further described later.)

Torch classification

Ordinarily, welding torches are classified according to the relative pressure of acetylene and oxygen, such as "low pressure," "balanced pressure," etc., referring to the pressure of acetylene used as compared to the oxygen pressure. The pressure of both gases is governed by the tip used, and it is advisable to become thoroughly familiar with the best working pressure, so that the greatest heat value is obtained from the gases consumed, and the flame is more easily controlled. The torch manufacturer has carried out a very elaborate series of experiments in order to prepare recommendations as to the proper size of tip to select for welding metal of a given thickness.

Another good reason for using the pressures recommended by the manufacturer for each size of tip is that it guards against burning of gas inside the torch. The gases being mixed within the torch, either in the handle or in the head, form a very combustible mixture.

If the pressure is strong enough to force the gases out of the torch tip at a speed higher than the speed at which the flame can travel, there can be no "popping." However, if the right pressure is not supplied the flame may travel back into the torch faster than the gases travel out of it and, in addition to popping, may continue to burn on the inside and damage the interior of the torch. For this reason also, the operator should be warned against increasing the size of the opening in the tip. This will be equivalent to using insufficient pressure for the size of hole in the tip indicated.

The preceeding discussion about the careful proportioning of various parts of the torch, and particularly the careful calibration of the gas passages, should be sufficient to indicate the need for handling the torch as a precision instrument. Some operators are careless enough to use a torch for a hammer or for a pry and try to avoid changing tips by increasing the size of the opening in one tip. Others will neglect to blow out the apparatus before using it, thereby permitting dirt to lodge in the gas passages and to obstruct them.

Such treatment can only result in poor operation and, occasionally, in such a poor mixture of the gas that the weld is made at a considerably greater expense than would be necessary if the torch were kept in first-class condition.

Torch cleaning

The proper way to clean the passages of the torch when they have become clogged with dirt or carbon (as the result of popping) is to disconnect the hose and blow out the passages from the head. Using a blast of oxygen is best. If the tip is clogged and cannot be blown out readily, it can be cleaned by using a *soft copper wire* or a tip cleaning drill of the correct size.

In general, remember that the welding torch and the welding regulator are precision instruments and require careful handling to keep them in good working order. It is poor practice to use any such piece of apparatus for purposes for which it is not intended, such as using an oxygen cutting regulator for welding, or trying to do cutting with a *welding* torch by turning on excess oxygen. Combination torches are made which permit going from welding to cutting with slight adjustments, but the operator should never attempt to do this unless he has equipment designed for this purpose.

The well equipped welding shop will contain a number of accessories which are practically indispensable for efficient operation.

One of the first results of improper handling of the welding torch is the development of leaky valves. Leaky valves are both dangerous and wasteful and should be repaired immediately. If there is any doubt at all about the conditions of the valves, they can be tested by closing them and watching the low pressure gauges on both regulators. If either hand drops quickly, a leaky valve is almost certain to be the cause. The cylinder valve, of course, should be closed when this test is made. It is very difficult to repair a leaky valve by grinding because the fit has to be so exact that, as a rule, very fine machine work is required. This can usually be done best only at facilities operated by the manufacturer of the torch. Very often a complete replacement is more economical than a repair.

When leaks occur around the tip of the torch, the trouble can usually be traced to overheating, but occasionally it is due to carelessness in assembling the torch; the operator did not take care to see that the tip and threads were clean before inserting them in the head. Leaks may also be caused by allowing tips to lie loose in the drawer or on the bench with other tools where they will get bumped or scratched. The careful operator will provide a suitable rack on which all tips can be kept away from possible damage, and where the proper size can be easily selected.

TORCH LIGHTERS

Another essential part of the equipment is the friction spark lighter, used for safely lighting your torch. There are several types of lighters on the market, and the most economical model consists of a simple spring wire han-

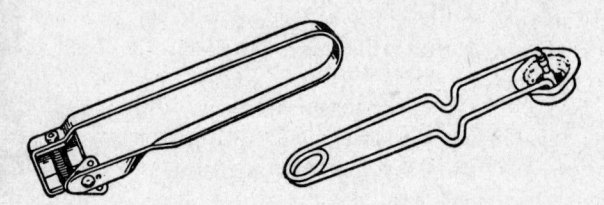

Fig. 5—There are many kinds of spark lighters.

dle, which holds a flint against a short file. The file is enclosed in a cup (Fig. 5) which traps the heavy acetylene gas to insure immediate combustion.

CAUTION: **A spark lighter should always be used for lighting the torch; never use matches or an open flame for this purpose. When igniting, always be sure that the torch tip is pointed away from your body or other combustible material.**

WELDING FLUXES

When most metals (other than steel) are welded, it is generally necessary to use a flux. Flux is a chemical preparation which helps prevent the formation of harmful oxides in the puddle of the weld metal, cleanses the molten metal of impurities, and prevents violent chemical reactions which might occur in different metals at the high temperatures of welding. They are usually supplied in powdered form, and may be used as supplied, or as a liquid or paste.

While many fluxes have relatively simple formulations, there is seldom any economy in making them yourself. Few shops have the facilities for proper mixing, and a poorly-made flux is practically worthless.

Some fluxes lose their effectiveness if exposed to the atmosphere for a long time, and thus should be kept in airtight containers from which only enough flux for a day's work should be removed at one time. Other fluxes, after use, leave hard deposits which may have to be ground off before finishing work is done. Still others have chemical properties which requires they be washed from the surface of the weld after it is completed. The instructions for each flux should be followed to the letter to get good results.

When selecting a flux, be certain to use a good one, and be sure it is compounded especially for the metal you are welding. Do not attempt to weld without a flux if a flux is needed, since the resulting weld probably will be worthless. Keep a working supply of flux in a flat, heavy container that will not tip, and keep the main supply covered so that it will remain clean.

PORTABLE GRINDERS

The portable grinder is an exceptionally valuable, auxiliary tool for the weldor. If it is used before welding to bevel out and clean the edges to be welded, better penetration is secured. The welding itself also is easier and more economical than working on dirty metal. After welding, it is often desirable to dress the work down with a grinder to improve its appearance, or to permit good finishing to be done. A grinder is also useful in preparing the edges of welded test specimens for acid etching.

Likewise, there is much to be said for sand and shot blasting. While many weldors do not appreciate this point, these are splendid devices for cleaning surfaces to be welded. In production welding departments, it is quite common to find parts prepared for welding through sandblasting or shotblasting. Either is an exceptionally good way to prepare iron and steel parts which are to be welded with bronze.

ASBESTOS

Asbestos is used in the welding shop in two forms — paper and powder. No repair welding establishment could be considered complete without a roll of asbestos paper. This is used as a cover for firebrick in preheating furnaces or as a cover for parts which have been welded and require slower-than-usual cooling. It serves as a protection to shield the weldor from the intense heat of welding heavy (thick) sections, as protection for adjacent parts when broken machinery is being repaired where it stands, and has protection to the finish of automobiles when body repairs are being completed.

The powder has a wide range of similar uses, making it extremely valuable on both large and small work. In many cases it can be substituted for carbon if the latter is not available.

PREHEATING DEVICES

Several kinds of preheating equipment are available for the weldor, and often he may employ two or more for a single job. Preheating simply means the heating of the piece or pieces to be welded before initial welding. Preheating may be done on an entire piece, or confined to only a portion of it.

One reason for preheating is to raise the temperature of the areas to be welded sufficiently high that the actual welding will require the minimum of gas and time. Another is to expand the whole piece, or part of it, so that

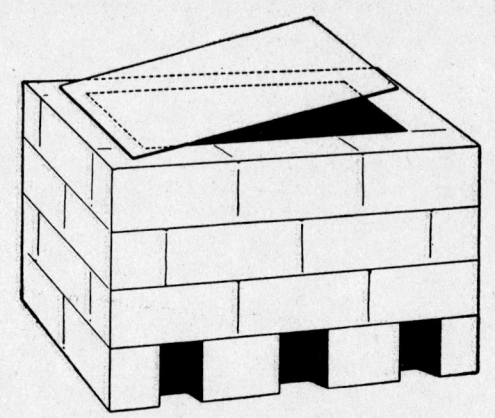

Fig. 6—Charcoal preheating furnace.

when the weld metal cools and shrinks, the shrinkage will be even and the contraction strains will not cause a break somewhere.*

With a supply of loose firebrick and a sheet of asbestos paper, the weldor can build a charcoal preheating furnace admirably suited to many preheating jobs. (Fig. 6.)

Probably the most satisfactory method of preheating is provided by the so-called liquefied petroleum gases used for domestic cooking where city gas is not available. These gases are commonly known as LP-gas, "bottled-gas" or "tank-gas". They are abundantly rich in heating

---
*This subject is discussed more in detail in Chapter 6.

value, and are available in cylinders from dealers in almost any town in the country.

Propane (bottled-gas) has a boiling point of —44° F, while butane (tank-gas) has a boiling point of +30° F. A standard cylinder of propane contains 100 lbs of liquid fuel by weight, which, when vaporized, is equal to 850 cu ft of gas. At 70° F (room or usual summer temperature) the cylinder pressure of the gase is approximately 125 psi.

LP gas preheating torches are widely available on the market. These torches have a type of mixer which draws air from the atmosphere to produce highly efficient, clean flame which is readily adjustable in size. Compressed oxygen, therefore, is not required. A typical outfit of this kind is illustrated in Fig. 7.

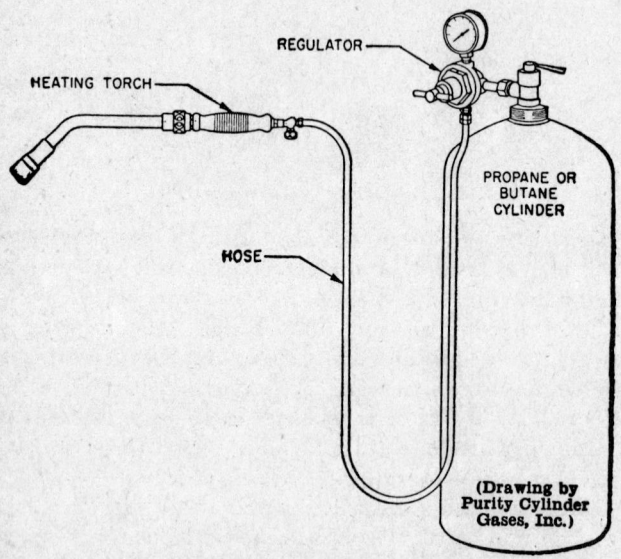

Fig. 7—A typical LP gas preheating outfit.

This method of preheating is clean, portable, economical, safe and the volume of heat produced is adjustable over a wide range. LP gas eliminates all the objections which are common to coke, charcoal or oil preheaters.

There is also a type of city-gas oven consisting of several parallel pipes working off a common header, and covered by a sheet metal hood which can be raised or lowered. For some jobs, an excellent arrangement is a

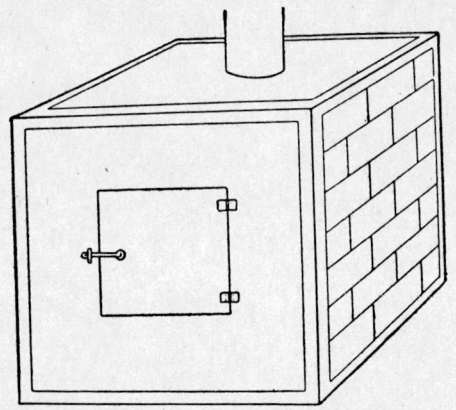

Fig. 8—Preheating oven (can be used for annealing).

permanent firebrick oven, heated by a blast from one or more gas or oil burners. (Fig. 8.)

Comparatively few welding shops have been equipped with all of these types of preheating equipment but, as a rule, every large shop will have two or three different procedures available so that a desirable choice of methods can be made. Some of this equipment can be purchased at very reasonable prices, other devices can be made at small expense from scrap materials.

CAUTION: **Never use compressed oxygen as a substitute for compressed air in any kind of preheating device.**

Some welding jobs require annealing after the welding is finished. Very often the equipment used for preheating can be used for annealing, but occasionally it is advisable to have special annealing ovens. However, investment in this equipment is not justified unless there is someone in charge who is familiar with the principles of heat treating.

CARBON

Carbon, in the form of plates, blocks, rods, and paste, has countless uses in the repair welding shop. It can be used for molds when building up lugs, bosses, gear teeth,

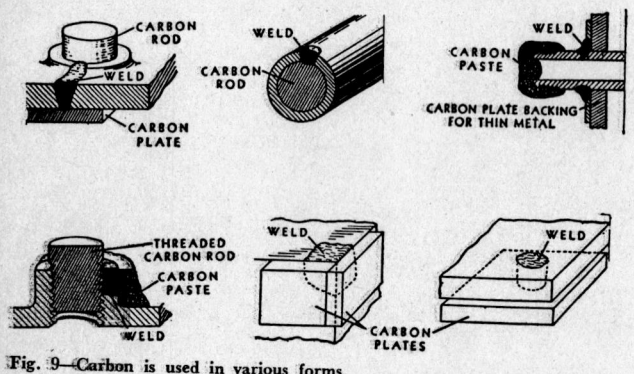

Fig. 9—Carbon is used in various forms.

etc. Rods can be used to protect threads in holes, and to allow building up around a hole. The paste is often used as a support for small parts to be welded. (Fig. 9.)

WELDING RODS

Whenever parts that are being welded are more than $3/32$-in. thick, it is necessary either to separate the edges or to bevel them down so as to provide an open space. This permits welding at the bottom, and thus assures complete penetration of the fusion process throughout the thickness of the material.

It is obviously necessary to provide some material to fill in this gap. This is done by melting into the weld some additional material. The standard way of doing this is to use a metal rod, known as a welding rod or filler rod, which is melted right into the weld.

Filler Rod Selection

A great portion of the success of the welding operation depends upon the selection of the proper material for the filler rod. It is possible to fill up the gap with any kind of metal which may be available, but if the rod selected is not suitable for welding, the resulting job will be of poor quality and, in fact, may be totally unsatisfactory.

Next to the development of torches and regulators and methods of producing high purity gases and good quality carbide, all of which has been done as a result of years of costly research, comes that of welding rods. They have been developed through years of effort by a number of the finest metallurgical laboratories in the world. The weldor cannot afford to bypass the knowledge which has been gained through these studies. He is not obliged to know all the scientific aspects of this work in detail. He can benefit just as much by taking care to see that the source of supply for his filler rod is a reputable house, which offers to the market a standard, trade marked product. The standard brands of filler rods on the market are the result of the aforementioned years of metallurgical investigations. The inexperienced weldor will do well to let a reliable firm recommend the right filler rod for each specific job.

For the general run of repair and production work, it

is generally assumed that the metal in the filler rod should be of the same general character as the metal which is being welded, i.e., mild steel should be welded with mild steel welding rods, cast iron with cast iron welding rod, bronze with bronze welding rod, aluminum with aluminum welding rod, etc. The welding rod should be of a character and composition which will give, after welding, a weld metal of the same physical and chemical properties as the base metal.

In cast iron welding, for example, a welding rod with a generous amount of silicon in it is recommended. The rod itself will probably be of a better grade of material than a good many iron castings. In this case, the silicon in the rod is a distinct aid to the welding.

For another example, take ordinary rolled steel plate. This material has had mechanical treatment which refines the grain structure, whereas the metal deposited from the rod will have some of the characteristics of cast metal. Thus, it is not possible to select the welding material which, when cast into the bevel, will show exactly the same composition and structure as the parent metal. Or, it may be desirable to secure a weld which is especially strong; this can be done by using a special alloy steel welding rod.

Choosing a Filler Rod

In order to be able to make a satisfactory selection of filler rod, the weldor should study this subject from two viewpoints — first, chemical analysis, and, second, weldability. The chemical analysis of filler rod tells what elements are included in its composition and their proportions. For some kind of work, different specifications have been made as to chemical analysis.

For welding mild steel, structural shapes, plate, bars or low carbon steel forgings and castings, the following is a common specification for a satisfactory welding rod:

FOR WELDING MILD STEEL

Carbon ......not over 0.16%   Sulphur ......not over 0.04%
Manganese ...not over 0.15%   Silicon ....not over 0.08%
Phosphorus ....not over 0.04%

For welding high carbon steel and worn surfaces where great resistance to abrasive wear is desired and where machining is not necessary, such as rails, switch points, bearing surfaces, etc., the following analysis is common:

FOR WELDING HIGH CARBON STEEL

Carbon ....0.06-0.75%   Phosphorus ...not over 0.04%
Manganese ....0.60-0.90%   Sulphur ......not over 0.04%

A filler rod for mild steel which will produce greater strength but lower ductility might have the following analysis:

FOR WELDING NICKEL STEEL

Manganese ....0.50-0.80%   Nickel 3.25-3.75%
Phosphorus ...not over 0.04%   Carbon 0.15-0.25%
Sulphur ....not over 0.04%

FOR WELDING CAST IRON

Carbon ....3.00-3.50%   Silicon 3.00-3.50%
Manganese ....0.50-0.75%   Sulphur 0.10%
Phosphorus 0.50-0.70%

Aluminum filler

For welding aluminum, where great ductility is required, a rod containing 99% aluminum is recommended. But for the general welding of aluminum a rod containing 5% silicon and 95% aluminum is often recommended.

The special chemical analysis serves the primary purpose of avoiding the use of filler rods which contain too high a percentage of undesirable impurities. For example, when carbon and manganese are kept low, there is less tendency for the fused metal to boil and form blow holes.

The weldor should realize, however, that he cannot secure a perfect welding rod merely by specifying a certain chemical analysis. There may be other impurities present in metal which is not made specifically for welding, which do not show in the analysis and which will remain in the weld to weaken it. If there is an excess of such impurities, the weldor has to spend a lot of time manipulating the rod and flame to float them to the surface so that they will not be trapped in the weld puddle when it solidifies.

Filler Rod Testing

It is not possible for the average weldor to test his filler material for chemical composition, since this has to be done in a metallurgical laboratory. He can, however, insist that the analysis be guaranteed by the manufacturer. He can also test the welding quality of each supply of filler rod delivered to him. It takes only a few minutes to melt a short piece of rod and determine immediately whether it melts readily and flows smoothly, without excessive boiling and without showing excessive amounts of impurities which will have to be worked out.

Where a considerable amount of welding is involved it is good practice to make a systematic test of every kind of welding rod purchased. A record of this test should give the following information:

Filler Rod—Manufacturer; Description; Composition; Diameter; Finish. **Parent Metal**—Composition; Thickness; Design and Position of Weld. **Torch**—Manufacturer; Style and Size; Tip Tize Used; Gas Pressures Used; Character of Flame; Distance of Inner Cone of Flame from the Metal. **Welding Characteristics**—How the Metal Flows under the Flame; Fusion with Parent Metal; Flux Used, if any; Tendency to Boil. **Weld**—Appearance; Amount of Scale; Difficulty of Removing Scale; Appearance of Metal Beneath Scale; Dimension of Deposit; Tensile Strength; Ductility. **Fracture**—Appearance of Deposited Metal; Number of Blow Holes; Slag Inclusions; Penetration; Fusion with Parent Metal. **Name of Operator Making the Test.**

Selecting the Right Size

Another important consideration is the selection of the proper size welding rod. Too large a welding rod will chill the puddle and make fusion difficult, whereas too small a rod does not work into the pool rapidly enough and too much time is required to make the deposit.

There is so much similarity in the appearance of welding rods that special precaution should be taken to prevent rods of different kinds being mixed together. Racks or bins should be provided, with compartments for each kind. They should be plainly marked so that in no case will the wrong filler material be used by mistake. Many unnecessary failures have been caused in welding on account of this simple case of "mistaken identity".

CHAPTER 4
SETTING UP YOUR EQUIPMENT

It is perfectly obvious that in order to get the best results from the oxy-acetylene welding outfit and at the lowest operating expense it is necessary for the operator to become thoroughly familiar with the handling of the different units and with the proper method of assembling them in preparation for the day's work. Even in large plants where there are a great many welding torches, and operators are constantly coming and going, it is a poor plan to depend upon a foreman or supervisor to get the torch all ready for action and put it into the hands of the weldor. In each case, the weldor should know how to make the assembly and get under way. He should also be fully informed on the proper methods of taking care of all parts of the equipment so that they will be always kept in first class working condition.

In order to get a complete outline of the proper method of assembling the welding equipment, it is well to assume that fresh cylinders of oxygen and acetylene are ready at the welding station and that the equipment is all disassembled and packed properly in a storage or carrying case.

Fasten Cylinders Securely

The first step in setting up an oxy-acetylene welding outfit is to remove the valve protecting caps from the oxygen cylinder and the acetylene cylinder if it has one. These caps should be placed where they will be readily found when the cylinder is empty. The cylinders should now be fastened securely on the truck by means of a chain lock (Fig. 1) so that they will not tip or fall. If a truck is not used the cylinders should be lashed together and secured against a post or column to insure against their falling.

Fig. 1—Fasten cylinders securely in truck by means of chain lock so that they cannot tip or fall.

In order to make sure that the cylinders are full of gas and the valves in good working order, the welding operator should "crack" the valves (Fig. 2.). By "cracking" is meant the opening of the valve slightly, allowing enough gas to escape to blow out the valve passage outlets, thereby any rust, dust or foreign material that

Fig. 2—"Crack" oxygen and acetylene valves momentarily to blow out any foreign matter that may have become lodged in the valve outlet.

may have become lodged in the valve outlet while in transit or storage is removed *Caution!* Do not open valves more than a quarter turn nor leave them open for more than one or two seconds. They should not be closed so tightly that it requires great effort to reopen them.

Fig. 3—Attach oxygen regulator after making certain that valve is free of foreign matter. Use forged steel wrench provided in outfit for this purpose. Never use pipe wrenches, pliers or ill fitting wrenches which wear off hexagonal portion of connecting nut, making it impossible to secure a tight connection.

SETTING UP EQUIPMENT

Attach Regulator

Attach the oxygen regulator to the oxygen cylinder (Fig. 3) and the acetylene regulator to the acetylene cylinder (Fig. 4). In each case be sure that the valve is free of foreign matter. Note that each connection to the cylinder is different, so that there is no possibility of attaching the wrong regulator to the wrong cylinder. Use the forged steel wrench provided in the welding

Fig. 4—Attach acetylene regulator. Again be sure that connections are clean. Use forged steel regulator wrench only.

outfit for tightening the connecting nut. Never use a pipe wrench, pliers or other ill fitting wrenches which will wear the hexagonal portion of the connecting nut, making it difficult or impossible to secure tight connections. This is extremely important—do not use excessive force in tightening the regulators in place. *Caution!* Be sure that greasy gloves are not worn when attaching the oxygen regulator. Also be sure that there is no grease on the wrench.

Blow Out the Hose

The green hose, which has a righthand thread connection, should be attached to the oxygen regulator. Then attach the red hose with the lefthand thread connection

Fig. 5—Attach green oxygen hose with right hand thread to oxygen regulator. Attach red acetylene hose with left hand thread (notched hexagonal nut) to acetylene regulator with torch wrench furnished with outfit. Do not tighten excessively.

(notched hexagonal nut) to acetylene regulator. Use the proper opening in the torch wrench furnished with the outfit to tighten these nuts. Do not tighten with excessive force, but be sure they are sufficiently tight to prevent any possibility of gas leakage. The adjusting screws on both regulators should be released so as to take all spring pressure off the regulator diaphragm. The oxygen

56 SETTING UP EQUIPMENT

regulator screw is adjusted by turning it counterclockwise until it turns freely (Fig. 6). The acetylene regulator screw is released likewise.

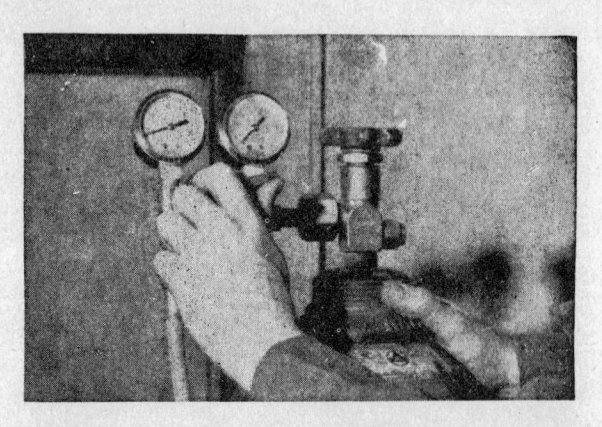

Fig. 6—Release oxygen regulator adjusting screw by turning counterclockwise until it turns freely.

OXY-ACETYLENE WELDOR'S HANDBOOK 57

The cylinder valves should now be opened one at a time. They should be opened very slowly, as is shown in Fig. 7. Having opened the cylinder valve there is now pressure on the regulator diaphragm. By turning the oxygen regulator adjusting screw clockwise, oxygen is released into the hose to blow out the talc. This operation should be repeated with the acetylene regulator so as to blow out the acetylene hose (Fig. 8). It is very

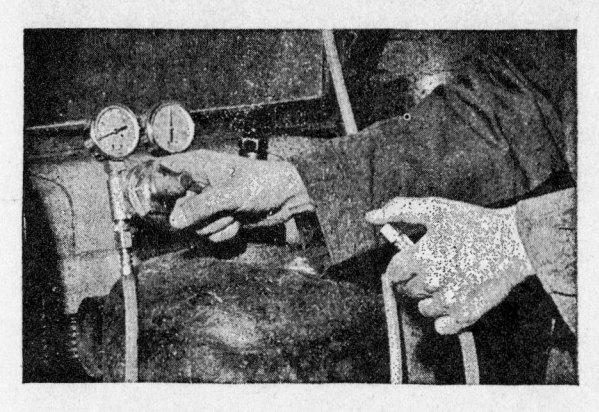

Fig. 8—Turn oxygen regulator adjusting screw clockwise until oxygen flow blows out the hose. Repeat with acetylene regulator adjusting screw to blow out acetylene hose. Do this quickly and avoid discharging a large volume of acetylene to avoid producing an inflammable mixture.

easy for dust to collect on the inside of the hose, and it is better to blow it out than to take chances on having it carried into the gas passage of the torch, where these particles may stick and cause trouble. For this reason the welding hose should be blown out each time the outfit is connected. *Caution!* When blowing out the acetylene hose do it quickly to avoid discharging a large volume of acetylene. Keep the end of the hose away from open flames and have proper ventilation to avoid producing an inflammable mixture.

Blow Out the Torch

It is also possible that some dust or dirt may have found its way inside the torch since it was last used. Therefore, it is a good plan to open both needle valves of the torch (Fig. 9), insert the oxygen hose in the head

Fig. 9—Open both torch valves wide.

of the torch and turn on a little oxygen to blow out the interior of the torch (Fig. 10.). The operator should immediately connect the oxygen and acetylene hose to the torch (Fig. 11), making sure that all connections are tight and clean, and that the proper hose connection has been made. If the above procedure is followed carefully it is reasonably certain that all gas passages are now clean.

Select the Correct Tip

Now consult the instruction chart which comes with the torch and select the tip which is of the right size for the work to be done. Also note from the chart what gas

OXY-ACETYLENE WELDOR'S HANDBOOK 59

Fig. 10—Blowout torch with oxygen by placing oxygen hose connection against the outlet of the torch head.

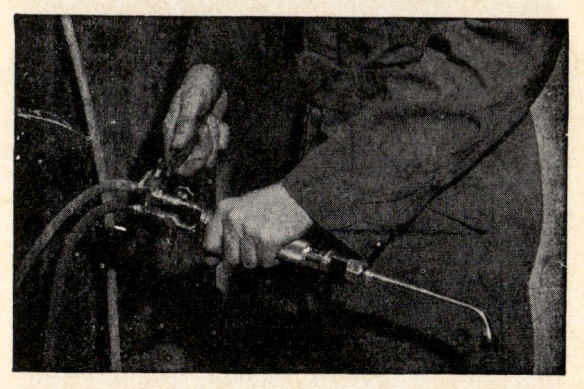

Fig. 11—Connect hoses to the torch inlet valve, using proper opening on torch wrench furnished with outfit.

pressures are recommended for a tip of the size selected. After inspecting the tip to make sure that it is clean and that there are no obstructions in the inside, insert it in the torch head and tighten it with the wrench just enough to make it gas tight (Fig. 12.).

Fig. 12—Select and insert proper size welding tip. Use proper opening on torch wrench. *Important!* Do not tighten with excessive force—it is not necessary.

Adjusting the Flame

The outfit is now all ready for operation except turning on the gas and adjusting the flame. Open the needle valves of the torch and turn the oxygen regulator adjusting screw until the low pressure gauge shows that oxygen is being delivered at the desired working pressure (Fig. 13), then close the oxygen needle valve. Now open the acetylene needle valve of the torch and turn the regular adjusting screw until the desired acetylene pressure is shown on the low pressure gauge (Fig. 14).

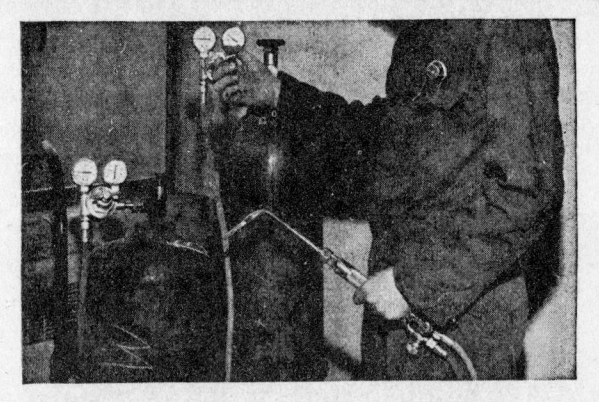

Fig. 13—Consult pressure chart. Adjust oxygen flow pressure with torch valve open. Then close valve.

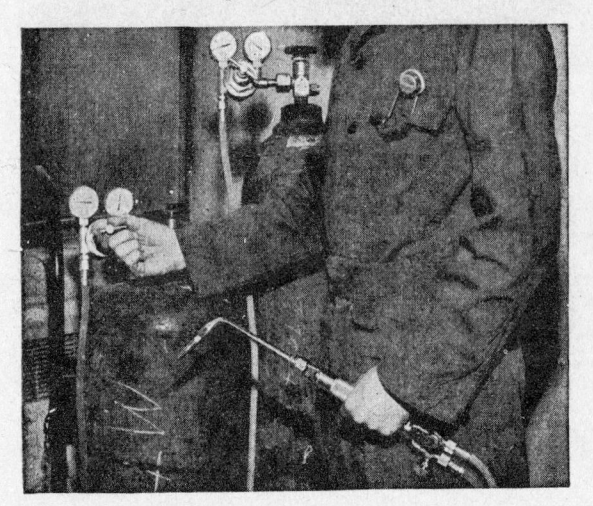

Fig. 14—Adjust acetylene flow pressure with torch valve open. Then close valve.

The torch is now ready to be lighted with a friction lighter. Avoid the use of matches or open flames as far as possible. Point the tip of the torch away from your body, by-standers, other workers or combustible material. Open the acetylene needle valve about one-quarter turn and light the escaping gas at the tip end. Now, still further open the acetylene needle valve so that the

Fig. 15—Point the torch tip away from your body, by-standers, other workmen or combustible material. Turn on acetylene at torch inlet valve and light the torch with the safety spark lighter furnished with outfit. Never use matches.

pure acetylene flame is sufficiently large to produce a velocity that will not release any free carbon or soot into the air. This flame condition is shown in Fig. 15 When this adjustment is secured open the oxygen needle valve on the torch and adjust the oxygen pressure (Fig. 16) until two distinct types of flames are plainly visible. The first flame, a small white perfectly smooth cone, directly in front of the tip, is surrounded by a second flame, a bushy envelope. This combination is called the

Fig. 16—Turn on oxygen by opening torch inlet valve gradually. Adjust for neutral oxy-acetylene flame.

neutral flame and is the correct adjustment for most welding operations.

Three Flame Types

It will possibly be well at this time to discuss briefly the various types of flames which can be secured with the oxy-acetylene torch and also the important characteristics of several of these flames (Fig. 17.).

The first flame produced is the acetylene flame secured by burning acetylene in the air. This flame is very long

OXYACETYLENE FLAMES

The Acetylene Flame is produced by burning acetylene in air. This flame is very long and bushy giving off flakes of soot. While it is very hot it is not suitable for welding and too costly for heating.

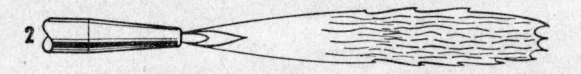

The Carburizing Flame is produced by burning an excess of acetylene. It can be easily recognized by the feathery edge of the white cone. This flame introduces excess carbon into the weld.

The Neutral Flame is produced by burning the correct mixture of oxygen and acetylene. The clear, well defined white cone indicates that the flame is correct. Welds made with it should be thoroughly fused and free from burned metal or hard spots.

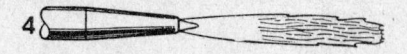

The Excess Oxygen Flame is produced by turning on excess oxygen, and can readily be recognized by its shorter envelope of flame and the small pointed white cone. Welding with this flame results in oxidizing or burning metal.

Securing the correct flame adjustment is the first step toward correct welding with the Oxy-Acetylene torch. The neutral flame must not only be established at the start of the welding operation, but it should also be maintained until the work is completed, because any appreciable deviation from thorough combustion of gases will result in introducing one of these gases into the molten metal.

and bushy and gives off a considerable amount of flaky soot which is easily visible, and which is practically nothing but uncombined carbon, i.e., the acetylene is so rich in fuel that there is not enough oxygen in the surrounding atmosphere to combine with it in combustion. Although this acetylene flame is fairly hot, it is not hot enough for any form of welding and it should not be used to any extent for any heating purpose because a similar amount of heat can easily be obtained with a less expensive fuel.

Carburizing Flame

Just as soon as pure oxygen is turned into the torch, the flame ceases to be an acetylene flame and becomes an oxy-acetylene flame. At first this takes the form of an excess-acetylene flame (Fig. 17). This name is given to it because there is more acetylene being supplied than will unite with the oxygen and consequently a certain amount of carbon is thrown off just as in the case of the simple acetylene flame burning in the open air, the difference being that there is not enough excess carbon to be as plainly visible. The excess-acetylene flame (or carburizing) is easily recognized by the fact that the white cone is shown just beginning to form but having a feathery edge instead of a sharply defined outline.

There are two facts regarding this type of flame which should be noted carefully by the weldor. First, fuel is being wasted because all of the acetylene is not consumed. Second, excess carbon is being introduced into the weld metal. As a general rule this has a detrimental effect. There are some cases where an excess-acetylene flame is specified for the express purpose of introducing carbon into the weld metal to secure a hard deposit, but this is only done on work of special kinds.

Oxidizing Flame

If oxygen is turned on to the point where there is an excess amount of oxygen, i.e., where there is more oxygen-supplied than will combine with the amount of acetylene which is being supplied, the result is an excess-oxygen (or oxidizing) flame (Fig. 17). This is easily recognized by the fact that the white cone begins to decrease in size and almost disappears if too much oxygen is turned on. The use of a flame with excess oxygen is very bad practice. The result is often spoken of as burning the metal and in fact this is what takes place when steel is welded with an excess-oxygen flame.

Enough has already been said about the affinity of oxygen for all metals at high temperature to indicate that the use of an excess amount of oxygen is bound to result in the formation of oxides in the molten metal. These oxides are just as detrimental to the strength of the bond as holes of the same size would be. In other words, a weld that is full of oxides is no stronger than one which has a spongy structure.

Neutral Flame

The neutral flame (Fig. 17) which has already been mentioned is the one in which the white cone is clearly outlined. When the welding flame has this appearance the operator can be sure that the oxygen and the acetylene are being furnished in the correct proportion to assure that neither gas is being wasted and what is more important, that the molten metal will not be injured by the introduction of any excess of either gas into it.

Neutral Flame Characteristics

It is customary to consider the neutral oxy-acetylene flame as consisting of two parts, namely; the white cone and the envelope, which have already been mentioned. However, some investigators have called attention to the fact that immediately surrounding the white cone and reaching out in a wedge shaped section into the envelope flame, there is a small faintly visible zone which has been called a reducing zone and which has an important bearing on the properties of the oxy-acetylene flame.

No attempt will be made to present a technical study of this feature of the welding flame at this point. It is sufficent to say that this so-called reducing zone is considered

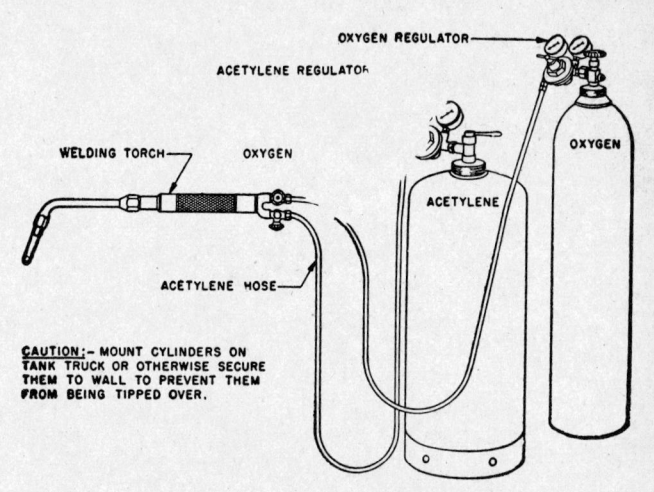

Fig. 18—The oxy-acetylene welding outfit.

to have important properties in connection with welding operations. It is further pointed out that an excess-oxygen flame does not show indication of the presence of this reducing zone. Consequently, it is obvious that this type of flame is lacking in one of the essential welding characteristics of the neutral flame. These considerations emphasize the importance of learning how to adjust the gas pressure so that the correct neutral flame is used at all times. It also emphasizes the importance of keeping the regulators and torches in good condition, because it is only when they are in good condition that they will deliver the gases uniformly, at the correct pressures. Any injury to the apparatus results in irregular deliveries of gas and will disturb the adjustment of the flame. If the operator is conscientious, he will religiously keep the flame neutral.

Packing the Outfit

The assembly of the welding outfit (Fig. 18) has been described in great detail because it is important that the equipment be handled so as to give it the best chances to work efficiently. To disassemble the outfit is of course somewhat less complicated. The torch is extinguished by closing the needle valves in the torch. If the outfit is not going to be used again immediately, the cylinder valves should also be closed at the same time. If the whole outfit is to be disassembled, the different parts should be packed in the carrying or storage case tightly and covered to avoid unnecessary accumulation of dust. The cylinder cap should also be replaced.

Preliminary Exercises

Assuming that the operator is getting his first experience in the handling of the oxy-acetylene flame, a few suggestions or a preliminary exercise may be helpful. Before assembling the apparatus it is advisable to set up the practice work on the welding table having a filler rod of the correct size at hand and making sure that there are no combustible materials left on the table. The operator should then familiarize himself with all the units and proceed to assemble the outfit as described above. He should then familiarize himself with the appearance of the different kinds of oxy-acetylene flames, both when wearing goggles and when not wearing them. He should not, however, melt any metal with the torch except when wearing goggles, because of the possible injury from flying sparks.

Observe Flame Effects

After observing the different kinds of oxy-acetylene flames, the operator can learn something about the action of these different flames by melting a small spot in a piece of sheet metal and advancing the molten pool along a straight line for a short distance, then observing the difference in the appearance of the metal melted by the three different types of flames, also observing how the molten metal behaves when it is being melted by the different type of flame.

Another good exercise at this time consists in melting the end of a filler rod held against a piece of sheet metal and carrying this along a straight line for a short distance so as to build up a little ridge of weld metal on top of the plate, making the same observations regarding the carburizing, oxidizing and neutral flames.

It is also instructive to a beginner to take a small piece of cast iron and repeat the above exercise with a cast iron filler rod, trying this first without the use of any flux and again using a good cast iron welding flux.

These simple exercises will illustrate to the beginner a few of the important fundamental welding principles which have already been stated, particularly the importance of flame adjustment and the necessity of using flux for welding all metals which require it. It is not necessary to carry these exercises very far or to melt a very considerable amount of metal in these experiments, provided the beginner is able to appreciate the fact that the difference observed in a small experiment may be greatly magnified when welding is done on a large scale.

Having learned to assemble a welding outfit and put it to use in the actual melting of metal the weldor should observe what factors are involved in the cost of any welding job, for it is only by observing economy in connection with all of these factors that any welding operation can be performed at the lowest possible expense.

Factors Affecting Cost

In general, it is true that the best workmanship will show the lowest cost figures on the total job. The basic cost figures are labor, gas and filler rod. The labor cost is reduced by acquiring sufficient skill so that no time is lost in going over the work, so that the whole welding operation proceeds at an even rate without interruption. The cost of gas is kept at a minimum by developing skill which allows the work to be done in the least possible time and which enables the weldor to use just the right amount of each gas to do the necessary amount of welding. Gas economies are also accomplished by keeping the apparatus in good condition and being constantly on the watch to prevent leaks in any part of the equipment. Real savings can also be made in the cost of filler rod by learning how to select the right material and right size for a given job and how to use only as much as is necessary on each job.

Sometimes weldors waste considerable time and gas in welding together short ends of filler rods in an attempt to save them. This does not always result in economy as the methods used may be more expensive than the material which would have been thrown away otherwise. The best way to save on welding rods is to learn to prepare the work correctly so as not to leave more space to be filled than is necessary and to use judgment in making a reenforcement on the top, so that material is not wasted by putting on more metal than is necessary.

CHAPTER 5
METHODS OF WELDING

Up to this point all attention has been directed toward getting the weldor thoroughly acquainted with the apparatus and materials used in oxy-acetylene welding, and with the proper methods of assembling the equipment and taking care of it. From this point, the next step is to learn the procedure of making a weld.

It is well known that a large part of the welding done by the oxy-acetylene process is on steel, particularly on mild rolled steel. Therefore, the instructions in this chapter will refer particularly to steel welding, unless otherwise specified, and special instructions for welding other metals will be given in later chapters.

Thin and Thick Sections

In very thin sections the welding process consists in melting both edges of the joint simultaneously and causing the liquid metal from both sides of the joint to flow together and then solidify into a solid homogeneous section. It is obvious that in the case of very thick sections a tremendous amount of heat would be required to penetrate to the bottom of such a joint if the two pieces to be joined were set close together, and that if they were separated so as to allow the flame to start at the bottom and work upward with the melting process it would be extremely difficult to control the melted metal so as to make it bridge the gap. For this reason the thicker sections (over $1/8$ in.) are beveled down from the top edge, allowing the parts to nearly touch at the bottom but leaving a good opening at the top. The gap thus formed is filled by using a filler rod, which is melted into the groove. Under these conditions there are three parts to be joined, the two sides of the joint and the filler rod. Good welding depends upon obtaining a solid union of all three into one piece.

Technique for Thin Sections

In the simplest case, then, two thin pieces are set edge to edge and it is desired to join them. Since the hottest part of the flame is just ahead of the white cone, the torch is held so that the cone does not quite touch the metal. The torch tip is directed forward so that the surplus heat from the flame will be thrown forward in the direction in which the weld is being made. The weld

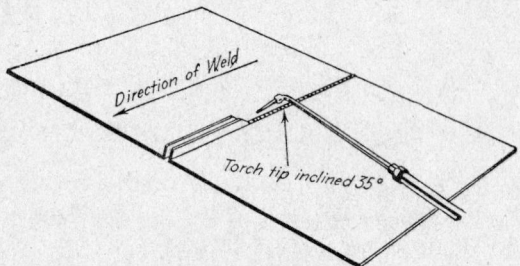

Fig. 1—Welding flanged edges.

will progress much faster than if the flame were slanted to the rear. A slight zig-zag motion of the tip will help work the edges together and also spread the heat far enough on each side the opening to be sure of melting both sides of it properly.

If the edges are set tightly together and not rigidly held in position, there will be noticed a tendency for one piece to draw up over the other as the weld progresses. This can be avoided by clamping or tacking the parts firmly in place or by separating them at the far end of the weld so as to form a very narrow vee. Disregarding this little difficulty at first, the operator should give all his attention to the subjects of fusion and penetration. Good fusion is indicated by clean solid metal throughout the joint, free from any kind of "worminess." Good penetration is indicated when the fusion has gone through so far that no trace of a crack can be seen on the reverse side, but rather a thin bead of metal.

Flange Edges of Thin Sheet

Sometimes thin sheet metal is prepared for welding by turning up shallow flanges along the edges, so that the weldor has only to melt down these flanges (Fig. 1). This makes the welding easy, but very poor work will result from careless procedure. If the melting is not complete enough there will be a crevice left on the reverse side of the weld and the top side will appear as a sharply rising hump of metal. Such a joint will not stand much bending. When the work is thorough it will be smooth on the bottom and the weld will slope off gradually to the sheet on top.

It requires very little practice to develop skill in handling the flame on thin sheets so that a smooth, regular, well penetrated weld is secured.

Bevel Thick Sections

When thicker sections are welded, requiring the use of a filler rod, a number of different types of work are encountered, and various methods of making the weld have been devised to suit the different conditions. However, the beginning of the weld is practically always the same. First the parent metal (the parts being welded) is well heated and then fused together at the bottom of the bevel, then the sides of the openings are melted down until a pool of molten metal is formed. The end of the rod is heated nearly to the melting point and introduced into the pool, where it is melted off gradually by the heat of the pool. *The rod should never be held and melted above the pool and allowed to drop into it a drop at a time.* As soon as the rod begins to melt and fill the gap, the flame is advanced slowly along the line of the weld, the end of the rod being kept in the pool, so that the pool of molten metal makes steady progress in the required direction.

Manipulation of Rod and Torch

As the thickness of the metal increases, the width of the gap or bevel increases, making it necessary to work the pool from side to side as well as straight ahead, in order to be sure of getting fusion with both sides. The best manner of doing this is a disputed point among the best of weldors. There are some who insist that this lateral movement of the pool is best accomplished by a swinging or zig-zag motion of the torch, and others who claim that the torch should advance practically straight and the rod used to manipulate the pool. Good work can be done either way.

Good Fusion with the Torch

If the weld consisted simply of filling in the groove, or bevel, with molten metal, this manipulation of the rod or torch would not be necessary. What the zig-zag movement does is melt down the walls on both sides of the joint, distribute the heat evenly and thoroughly, prevent the rod from blocking the heat away from the parent metal, and secure a complete fusion of the added material with the parent metal on both sides. Generally each lateral movement of the torch or rod is crescent shaped, producing a ripple effect in the surface of the finished weld.

Good Fusion with the Rod

The action of the rod during the operation is, to an experienced observer, a good indication of the degree of good fusion which is secured. If the rod seems to move smoothly and freely in the pool and there is no excessive boiling, the fusion is good; but if the pool seems to be sticky and the rod difficult to move, the heating is insufficient and the weld will probably show laminations or adhesions, that is, places where metal has stuck together without actual fusion. No matter whether the torch or the rod is used to control and direct the pool, the weldor must learn at the start *not to let liquid metal flow over onto solid or* plastic metal. This will only fill the groove without making a bond. It is a very common mistake with poorly trained beginners.

Important Principles

It will be helpful to beginners to summarize these fundamental principles of the welding operation into a few "welding rules," as follows:

Be sure the line of weld in the parent metal is heated to the proper melting point.

Heat the filler rod to the same melting point before introducing it into the pool.

Add the filler rod as evenly and steadily as possible.

Be sure that the added metal and parent metal are puddled together properly.

Keep the outer envelope flame playing over the pool, to protect it from the oxidizing influence of the air.

Melt a certain portion of the parent metal on both sides for the entire length of the weld.

Avoid reheating of weld metal which has cooled.

As to the methods of torch and rod manipulations, they are practiced in great variety. To the casual observer this appears at first to be a rather aimless movement but a study of the motions of a good weldor will show that they are systematic and purposeful.

Forehand Welding

Forehand welding and backward (or back hand) welding are such common terms that the weldor should

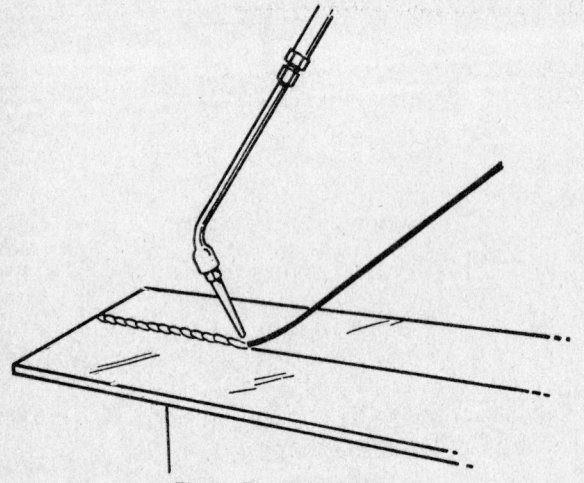

Fig. 2—Forehand welding.

familiarize himself with them and their meanings. In forehand welding (Fig. 2) the torch tip is inclined slightly forward in the direction of the weld and the rod is held ahead of the flame. It is evident that with the flame and rod in these positions the end of the rod keeps the heating zone from reaching the bottom of the crack just ahead of the pool. On thin material this is an advantage because it prevents melting through to such an extent as to cause a large gap, but on thick material it has the disadvantage of making it necessary to draw the rod too far away in order to let the heat work to the bottom, the rod becoming oxidized from contact with the air.

Forehand welding is therefore most generally recommended for welding lighter sections. The welding rod can be moved slightly to one side to allow the flame to reach the bottom in one direction, then a semi-circular movement of both rod and flame reverses the directions, avoiding contact of the tip of the white cone with the end of the rod. It is easier to learn this system if the movements of the torch and rod are practised separately at first.

Four Points to Watch

There are four points to check in this method of welding: (1) The heat must be allowed to penetrate to the very bottom of the crack for the whole length of the weld; (2) the white cone must be kept from touching the rod; (3) enough metal must be added so that the weld is full, and the added metal must be evenly distributed, and (4) the side of the weld should be practically parallel, indicating a uniform deposit.

Back Hand Welding

Back hand welding (Fig. 3 and 4) is accomplished by inclining the flame backwards and giving it only a slight transverse movement, the welding rod following the flame and being given a more pronounced transverse or semi-circular movement. The angle between the rod and the plane of the weld is usually about 45 deg. and that between the tip of the torch and the plane of the weld about 70 deg. On account of the position of the rod it can be seen that the ripples will be produced or shaped by manipulating the pool with the rod.

Advantages of Back Hand

Exponents of the back hand system of welding, particularly as applied to the welding of metal a quarter inch thick or more, claim that it has the advantage of making penetration and fusion more certain. In fact, one well known authority, who after refusing to consider this system for many years finally recommended

Fig. 3—Beginning a weld, back hand welding.
Fig. 4—Back hand welding.

it to a weldor who was having great difficulty with poor penetration, and had such excellent results that he required his entire force to adopt the system.

The better penetration is explained by the fact that the rod does not hinder the flame from reaching the bottom of the crack, or bevel. Better fusion is obtained because the rod is melted more positively into the pool, and it is not difficult for the operator to control the pool so that it does not flow over onto cooler metal. A further advantage claimed is that the pool is better protected by the envelope flame, which prevents the formation of oxides, and thus makes possible a more ductile weld. In addition, a smaller amount of beveling is required, the total angle being reduced to 60 deg. for thick work and 45 deg. on thin stock. This means faster work, with consequent savings in labor and gas, at no sacrifice of quality. If an operator has been accustomed to forehand welding and changes to the back hand method he will probably find that he will progress better with a slightly smaller filler rod for the same thickness of material. Do not select a rod that is too small, however, for it will burn easily and be difficult to distribute evenly, whereas too large a rod slows up the work.

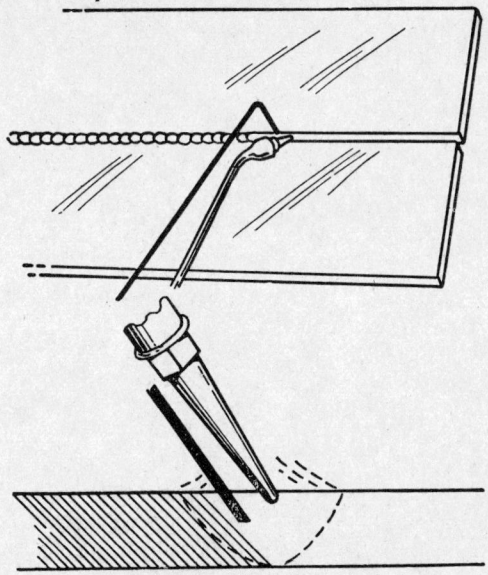

Fig. 5—Welding by rod manipulation.

Technique of Back Hand

The principal feature of the technique of back hand welding is the manipulation of the rod, which mixes and works the molten metal in the pool, prevents adhesions, and gets the rod out of the way so that the heating zone of the flame can melt the top portion of each ripple thoroughly. Proper manipulation of the rod will produce smooth, firm round ripples.

Method of Rod Manipulation

A technique which includes features of both forehand and back hand welding consists in slanting the flame forward and having the rod follow the flame and controlling the pool by rod manipulation. In this case the flame has a chance to preheat the metal adjacent to the crack, and the rod does not get in the way of it. At the same time, the envelope flame has ample opportunity to protect the rod and also the pool from oxidation by the air. Practically no lateral movement is given to the torch tip, but the rod takes a light wavy motion. Considerable

Fig. 6—Seam rewelded to make sure of penetration.

practice is required to obtain skill in maintaining a large pool the full depth of the weld, the tendency being to progress too fast, and to neglect keeping the end of the rod in the melting zone. If the pool is too small it can be enlarged by slowing up the motion of the rod. An obvious danger for the beginner is that of melting holes through the metal at the bottom of the crack. This can be corrected by advancing the rod slightly or drawing back the flame, or by changing the angle of the flame so that it points more forward and not so much downward, or possibly by working a head a little faster.

Double Welding

Double welding is a method highly recommended on thick sections when it is possible to use two operators at the same time. The edges are beveled from both sides, which immediately reduces the gap to be filled by one-half. It places the bottom of the weld, which is the weakest part of the weld, in the center of the section, which is the strongest part of the section; and if properly executed really does away with the bottom of the weld. The advantage of using two operators instead of having one operator weld first one side then the other, is that the metal adjacent to the weld does not have to be heated a second time, so there is a considerable saving in both time and gas. Sometimes a weld made from one side only, that is, beveled on one side only, is rewelded from the bottom to be sure of getting full penetration. This is good practice on welds which call for maximum strength, and not to be confused with "wash welding,"

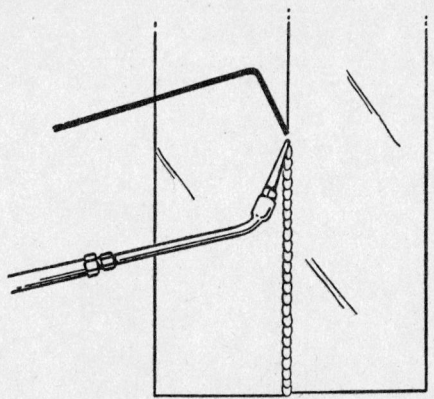

Fig. 7—Vertical welding.

a term applied to the habit of smoothing over a poorly penetrated job on the reverse side to conceal defective work.

Weld Position is Important

The fact that double welding, with two operators working simultaneously, is practicable only when the weld is in a vertical or horizontal seam suggests the importance of the position of the line of weld. This is emphasized by the fact that weldors who are accustomed to weld on large pipe often do not like to change to tank work which involves a great deal of flat welding. The pipe weld is usually made from the bottom of an upper quadrant up to the top of the pipe, the pipe being rolled as each half is finished in order that the weld may always progress upwards in this manner.

This position of the weld is helpful to speed, penetration, and fusion. Many other types of work can be made easier by placing the work on an incline, instead of flat, so as to take advantage of this position. It has been found especially helpful in the welding of iron and steel with bronze.

The Vertical Weld

The extreme case of working upward is the vertical weld (Fig. 7). The inference that penetration is easily

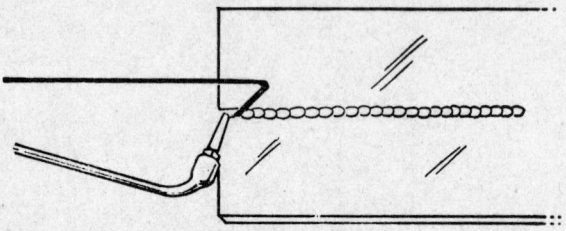

Fig. 8—Horizontal welding.

secured with the weld in this position is entirely correct. The vertical weld can be made either with the rod following the flame or the flame following the rod, but in the latter case the flame must be slanted forward considerably more to direct the heat ahead and prevent the back of the pool from running over instead of freezing into regular ripples. This running over of the metal is the greatest difficult found in vertical welding, and can be corrected only by practice to develop skill in handling the pool in this position.

The Horizontal Weld

Horizontal welding (Fig. 8) is the term usually applied to welding a horizontal seam in plates which are held in a vertical plane. It is a difficult weld to make because of the tendency of the pool to run down over the bottom edge and away from the top edge. Some weldors try to get away from this affect by welding successive overlapping pools. This may work well, but is quite apt to leave a number of pools poorly fused together. A continuous weld may be made if the operator is patient enough to master the technique. It is obvious that better results will be obtained if the pool is kept relatively small and not

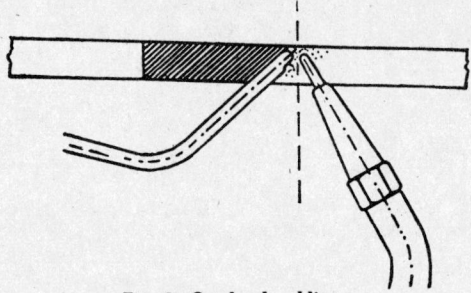

Fig. 9—Overhead welding.

so hot as in flat welding, because it will chill more easily. The rod may be manipulated so as to prevent the top edge from becoming excessively heated, so that the top edge of the pool will solidify quickly. Then if the flame is directed upwards the bottom edge will be prevented from melting too much, and the flame can be made to control the position of the metal in the pool to some extent.

The Overhead Weld

Overhead welding (Fig. 9) is difficult chiefly because the position is awkward for the operator. Control of the metal is soon acquired once he learns how to keep the pool from becoming so hot that it is too thin to handle easily. If this cannot be done by slanting the flame ahead of the pool, the chances are that the tip is too large.

The "Swish" Weld

Where a smooth surface is preferred to the rippled surface which results from the torch and rod manipulation described in the methods previously mentioned, a method called the "swish" weld is used on medium work. Here the tip is held nearly vertical to the plane of the work, with the rod slightly in advance of the cone. As the fusion point is reached a sharp forward movement swishes the metal ahead and leaves the surface comparatively smooth, so that little grinding is necessary for a smooth finish.

The "Fade-Away" Weld

On thin work a similar effect is obtained with the "fade-away" weld. The tip is inclined about 30 deg. to the work and the rod carried ahead of it and inclined about 45 deg. When the edges are ready to melt the rod is brought toward the torch and under the cone, the torch is brought forward with an upward turn, at the same time drawing the rod back. This lays successive drops with a herringbone effect. The method requires considerable practice.

Successive Pools

The method of welding by successive pools has already been suggested for cases where a continuous pool is difficult to handle. A pool is first formed of the correct size and the blast of the flame used to force most of the molten metal to the rear, where it is allowed to harden. Then the front edge of the first pool is taken as the center of the second pool, which is allowed to form, and filler rod is added, then this pool is worked backward like the first, and the process repeated until the weld is complete. This method is used a great deal on cast iron and aluminum work. Neat work results from making the pools of uniform size, and centered over the line of weld.

These various methods of manipulating the torch and rod in making a weld are the ones in most general use. A later chapter will discuss some of the most common defects found in welds imperfectly executed, but since some of these defects result as much from faulty preparation as from faulty procedure, the next chapter will deal chiefly with the preparation of the work before welding.

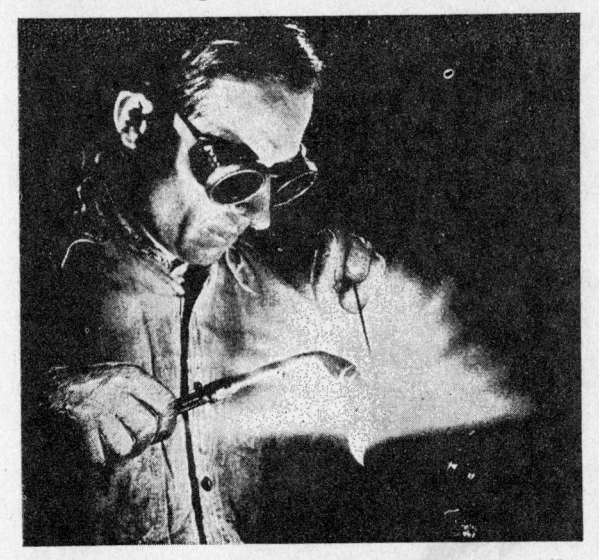

Welding provides a means of combining interesting skills.

CHAPTER 6
PREPARATION FOR WELDING

There are several different operations which may be considered under the general subject of preparation for welding which are fairly obvious to anyone who has read the previous chapters carefully. It is well for the beginner to know that there are quite a few considerations involved in the subject of preparation which might not occur to an inexperienced user of the torch, regardless of whether the welding is being done as a part of a general production program or whether it is being used in an emergency to repair some essential part of equipment which has been broken. A good deal of the chance for complete success depends upon the thoroughness of the preparation. This is particularly true if we consider preparation to include the planning of the entire job, as it should.

Location of the Weld

The man who is using the torch in production work has the advantage over the man who is using it simply to make repairs, because in production work it is possible to design the parts to be welded so that the weld can come at any desired part of the structure, the parts can be cut so that they are just the right size to fit together nicely and the general set-up for welding can be arranged so that the work will be in the most advantageous position.

The repair weldor has to weld a crack wherever it appears and has no control over its position, its direction or its convenience. Neither is it possible for him to arrange to have the weld come in place where the least amount of stress will be put on it. Since the conditions surrounding these two types of welding operations are so different, the subject of preparation will be discussed from the two different points of view.

Design Factors

It has already been indicated that in production welding the designer has considerable opportunity to make the welding easier and better. Therefore, the preparation for the work actually involves several things over which the weldor may not have direct control. The matter of design as considered here, means

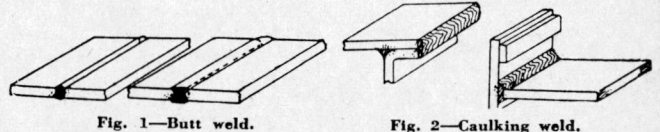

Fig. 1—Butt weld.   Fig. 2—Caulking weld.

not only the shape of the piece to be welded but also the location of the weld, the material specified to be welded, the selection of the filler rod, and the selection of the type of weld to be used. One of the most important factors of design is the location of the weld with respect to the rest of the structure. For example, in many cases it is not considered good design to have what corresponds to a single-vee weld in the corner of a tank, because the slight working of the sides which results from filling and emptying may eventually cause a fracture if there is the slightest crevice at the bottom of the weld where such a fracture can start. That is the reason why corner seams are so often avoided.

Select Proper Weld Type

Another mistake which may easily be made in design is that of using the wrong type of weld. It has several times been shown that special types of welds which had every appearance of being extra strong were actually weakened by the very features which were designed to give additional strength. A study of the more common types of welded joints will therefore be useful.

The Butt Weld

The butt weld (Fig. 1) is regarded by many authorities as the strongest types of weld when it is made

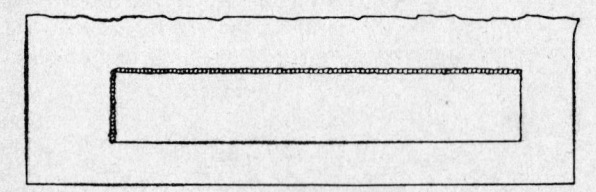

Fig. 3—Fillet weld.

properly. A butt weld is one in which two plates or surfaces are brought together edge to edge and welded along the seam thus formed. The two plates when so welded from a perfectly flat plane in themselves, excluding the possible projection caused by the reinforcement on the weld. This type of weld is used whenever possible in oxy-acetylene welding. It is of such importance that qualification tests for operators are usually based upon butt welded samples. The corner weld usually signifies the welding of two pieces which are set together with the edges at an angle. It is necessary to use filler rod and to use considerable skill in placing the metal to get a weld in this position which will stand hard service.

The Caulking Weld

A caulking weld (Fig. 2) is one made simply to close a seam against possible leakage. Such a weld may not be expected to stand very much stress but should be very superior to soldering because of its greater strength and the thoroughness of the bond between the parent metal and the deposited metal.

The Fillet Weld

The fillet weld (Fig. 3) is sometimes confused with the caulking weld but differs from it in that a fillet weld is expected to be much stronger. The fillet weld is one in which some fixture or member is welded to the face of a plate by welding along the vertical or horizontal edge of the fixture or member. The weld-

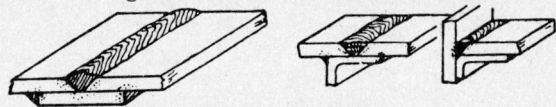

Fig. 4—Flush weld.

ing material is applied in the corner thus formed and finished at an angle of about 45 deg. to the plate.

The fillet weld when properly made consists of a single bead deposited so that it penetrates equally into both members. Since the cross section of the deposit is not equal to the cross section of the original metal,

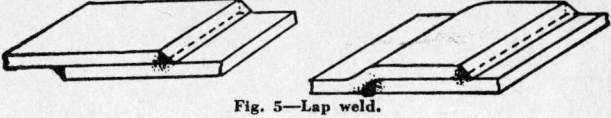

Fig. 5—Lap weld.

if the fillet is flat or concave, it is necessary to have an absolutely rigid joint between the original sections before the fillet weld is applied. If this is not done, the weld may be called upon to stand some of the stresses which are supposed to be taken up by other parts of the structure.

Technique of Fillet Welds

In the process of making a fillet weld, some difficulty is usually experienced by the operator at the start because the metal in the top edge of the weld attempts to run down or leave a depression along the upper edge of the weld in the parent metal. The weldor, therefore, must be careful not to use a flame which is too large and to direct the flame so that it has a tendency to force the metal upward, at the same time adding new metal from the filler rod along the top

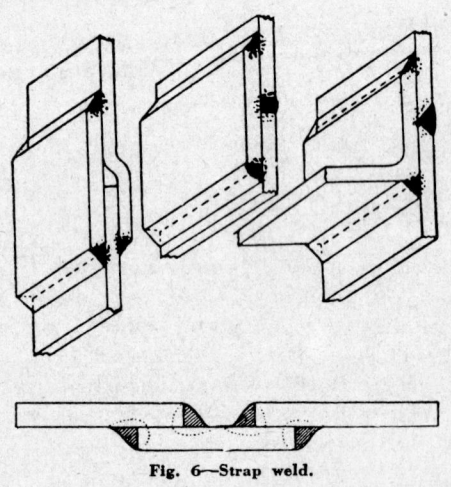

Fig. 6—Strap weld.

and letting it harden before it can fall away from the top edge. Care must also be taken to keep the bottom edge of the pool well fused with the bottom edge of the parent metal, so that there will be no chance for the liquid metal to run down on the metal which has not reached the fusion point. To get maximum strength in this type of weld, it is necessary to carry a wide pool so that the cross section of the weld will be equal to the thickness of the parent metal at all points.

The Flush Weld

The flush weld (Fig. 4) is one in which the top is finished perfectly flat or practically on the same plane as on the adjoining metal. It is not generally considered that this type of weld can be used where maximum strength is important, as a slight amount of reinforcement is a standard requirement for strength welds.

The Lap Weld

A lap weld (Fig. 5) is one in which the edges of two plates are set one above the other and the welding material so applied as to bind the edges of one plate to the face of the other plate. In this form of

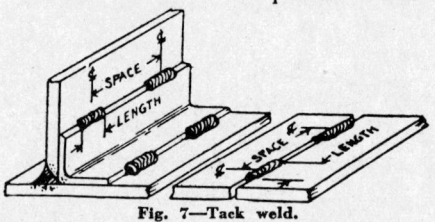

Fig. 7—Tack weld.

weld the seam or lap forms a raised surface along the entire extent. Where it is desired to do lap welding and maintain a perfectly smooth surface over several seams one of the plates can be formed along the edge so as to bring the top face on the level with the bottom side. Then, when the second plate is set to position it can be welded so as to get the desired smooth effect, provided more reinforcement is required.

The Strap Weld

A strap weld (Fig. 6) is one in which the seam of two adjoining plates or surfaces is reinforced by any form or shape to add strength and stability to the joint or plate. In this form of weld, the seam can only be welded from the side of work opposite from the reinforcement and the reinforcement, of whatever shape, must be welded from the side of the work to which the reinforcement is applied.

Fig. 8—Plain butt seam.

The Tack Weld

A tack weld (Fig. 7) is a short weld applied to the work in small sections to hold the two edges together so that the relative position of the edges is established before the final welding begins. Whenever the procedure involves the use of tack welds it is important for the designer to specify not only the length of each tack but also the distance from center to center of the tacks. Tack welding is used to a considerable extent in welding pipe lines. In this case the tacks should be placed

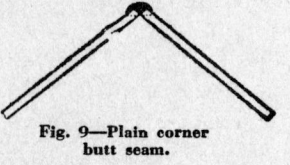

Fig. 9—Plain corner butt seam.

at the bottom of the bevel and when the weldor reaches them with his pool, he should make sure that he fuses all the way through to the bottom of each tack so that if his weld were cut open and examined no trace of the tack weld could be found.

Fig. 10—Single bevel butt weld.

Fig. 11—Double bevel butt weld.

The Plain Butt Seam

Some idea of the uses and relative merits of different types of welds may be gained from a study of their application in the welding of tanks and pipes. The plain butt seam (Fig. 8) is commonly used in the construction of tanks made of thin material. This joint can be made without any preparation of the parts and if the metal is not too thick, can be depended upon to show satisfactory strength. The same is true of the plain corner butt seam (Fig. 9). This joint requires the use of filler material to be reasonably strong and can be improved to a great extent by making a smaller additional weld on the inside.

Bevel Butt Welds

The single bevel butt weld (Fig. 10) shows the simplest design for butt welding sheet or plate material. Where strength is an important factor, this too, can be improved by running a small additional weld on the reverse side. It is generally considered, however, that the double bevel butt weld (Fig. 11) is more satisfactory for work 1/4 in. thick or more. It requires the making of two welds on each seam, but the total amount of deposit is much less than for a single bevel seam in the same thickness of metal and sometimes a lot of expense can be saved by making both welds simultaneously. Much of the success of this design depends upon the assumption the fusion will be carried all the way through the center, and the most frequent defect found when this method is used is an unwelded area in the center of the seam.

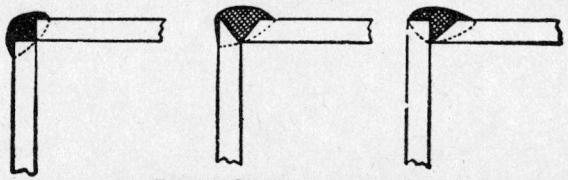

Fig. 12—Square corner seams.

The Square Corner Seam

The square corner seam (Fig. 12) is obviously a choice of design for getting a strong weld when making a right angle joint between thin plates. For most types of work it should be unnecessary to use any bevel, but the second method shown may be favored in some cases. However, the probability is that the third design will require less welding and give a stronger joint.

The Inside Lap Joint

The inside lap joint (Fig. 13) has frequently been offered as an ideal method of welding a bank bottom, but it has the obvious disadvantage of requiring considerable preparation. The two types of joints shown in Fig. 14 produce a very good construction when the weld is properly executed. This preparation of the pieces is a great aid to good penetration. It will be found, however, that it takes a rather skillful operator to handle such a design skillfully.

Flange Bottom Joint

For welding bottoms on cylinders, a design very much favored is the flange bottom (Fig. 15). This

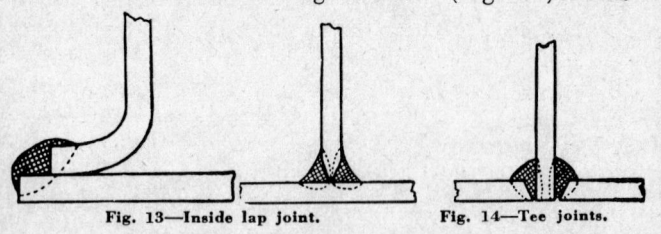

Fig. 13—Inside lap joint.   Fig. 14—Tee joints.

makes it possible to use either a single vee or a double vee butt weld. This construction is much favored by those who consider the butt weld to be the strongest type of weld.

Thick to Thin Sections

Sometimes it is necessary for the designer to include a butt weld made between pieces of different thickness. There are several ways to do this but the method shown in Fig. 16 is probably the most satisfactory.

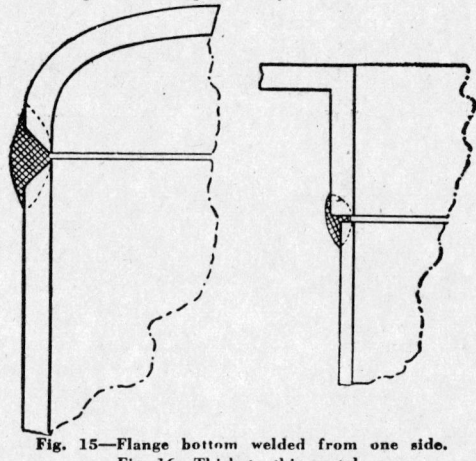

Fig. 15—Flange bottom welded from one side.
Fig. 16—Thick to thin metal.

It saves filler material and gives a better joint, provided the operator is careful to manipulate his torch so that both pieces are welded at the same time.

Joints for Pipe Welding

In pipe welding no difficulty is involved in the joints between straight lengths, these being in general,

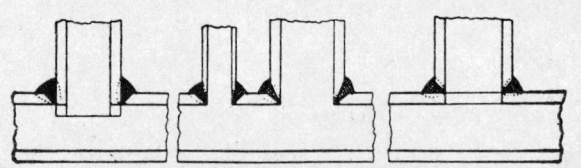

Fig. 17—Pipe nipples and manifolds.

ordinary butt welds. Fig. 17 shows methods of joining two pieces of pipe in the form of a tee and Fig. 18 shows methods of joining straight lengths at various angles. An exception is to be noted in the general statement made concerning the welding of straight lengths of pipe. This exception is in welding straight lengths of cast iron pipe with bronze filler rod instead

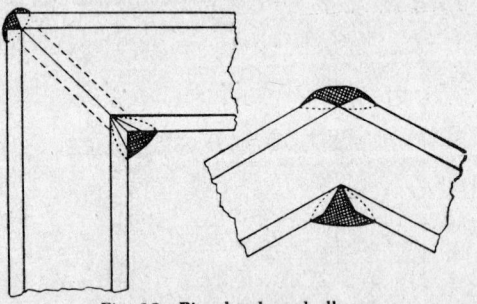

Fig. 18—Pipe bends and elbows.

of cast iron filler rod. When bronze was first used for this kind of joint, it was not considered necessary to bevel the edges of the pipe, but to simply butt it together, leaving a very small opening between the edges. The bronze was applied on the outside only no attempt being made to secure penetration through the pipe wall.

Welding Fittings

Recently there has been placed on the market a line of welding fittings. These forged steel fittings may be obtained in practically any form the pipe weldor might desire. There are elbows, tees, saddles, flanges, 180 deg. turns and concentric and eccentric reducers.

The use of welding fittings is preferred by many pipe weldors since it is generally recognized that better strength, lower costs and more efficient joints are obtained from their use. Welding fittings require only easy circumferential butt welds, which a pipe weldor can execute perfectly and economically. Welding fittings are usually made of seamless construction conforming to the specifications of the best seamless pipe. Their wall thickness is uniform throughout.

Bronze Collar Weld

In this case, the thickness of the deposit of bronze was always sufficient to give strength equal to that of the pipe itself and the strength of the joint depended upon the strong union between the bronze deposit and the outside wall of the pipe. In other words, it acted about the same as a coupling, without the disadvantage

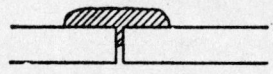

Fig. 19—Bronze collar weld. Fig. 20—Shear-vee weld.

present in the coupling or the necessity of cutting threads into the wall of the pipe. This type of joint was called the collar weld (Fig. 19).

Shear-Vee Bronze Weld

Careful studies of the collar weld have indicated that it results in a poor distribution of stresses when any pull is exerted on the pipe and a new design, called the shear-vee type has been introduced (Fig. 20). This design gives the joint the advantage of the penetration secured by the bevel and also the advantage of the bond secured on top of the pipe wall as in the collar weld. That is, it provides the strong shearing hold on the metal along with complete penetration of the bevel which enables the stresses to be transferred straight through the joint. From an operating standpoint, it has the advantage of requiring a somewhat smaller amount of metal.

Beveling is a subject of sufficient importance to deserve considerable emphasis in any discussion of welding. The purpose of the bevel, in both production welding and repair welding is to allow the weldor to start fusion at the bottom so as to be sure of getting full penetration (Fig. 21). The beginner seldom overlooks this part of the preparation, because it is either required of him or practice plates are supplied to him already beveled. But it is not uncommon to find experienced weldors who persist in trying to weld without beveling, and sometimes in production work beveling is omitted to save the cost of this operation

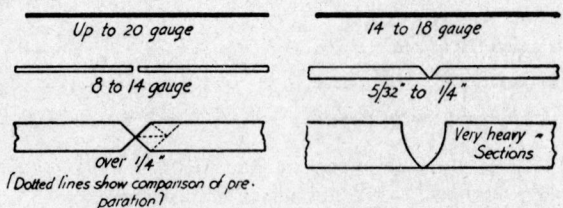

Fig. 21—Preparation of edges for different thicknesses.

on the material. Curiously enough, it is commonly found that failure to bevel properly is never admitted to be the cause of unsatisfactory welds.

Bevel for Penetration

When penetration is obviously necessary in order to secure a weld that is strong enough, beveling is the first step toward securing that penetration. A study of the literature of welding, especially that referring to the experiences of employers and supervisors who have had a chance to test the workmanship of a great many weldors, reveals the fact that by far the most common fault found with unsatisfactory weldors is that they do not get penetration. This is true of men who have welded for years, as well as of beginners.

Years of welding on metal which has not been properly prepared develops the habit of making the work look nice and smooth on the outside, with perhaps a good sound deposit nearly through the section. A weldor accustomed to work this way will instinctively concentrate his attention to the top of the weld instead of on the bottom. Qualification tests will pick out such weldors almost invariably. Furthermore, it has been demonstrated in actual field work that an inexperienced weldor who has learned to start at the bottom and fill a groove with sound metal will produce a joint which "pulls better" than poorly penetrated welds,

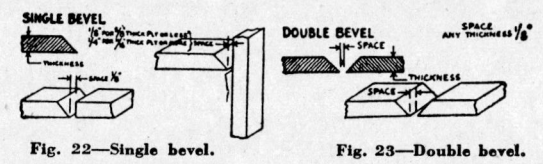

Fig. 22—Single bevel. Fig. 23—Double bevel.

although the work of the novice may look very ragged and weak from the top. The way to get the habit of starting from the bottom is to bevel the edges so that fusion *can* be started there.

Types of Weld Bevels

Single bevel (Fig. 22) is the term applied to the preparation when only one edge is beveled and from one side only. There are times when this partial preparation is necessary and sufficient. Double bevel (Fig. 23) is the term applied to the preparation when the edges of both pieces are beveled from one side only. When the material is thin, or when the weld can be made from one side only this is good preparation.

Single-V (Fig. 24) is a term applied to the prepara-

both sides. This preparation can be used only when it is possible to weld from both sides of the work.

Double-V (Fig. 25) is a term applied to the preparation when both edges are beveled from both sides, the welding, as in the previous case being possible from both sides. The depth of both bevels need not neces-

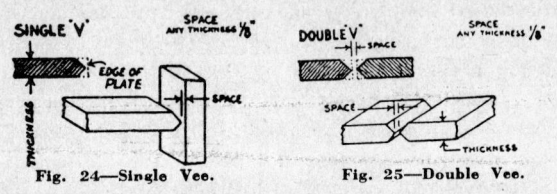

Fig. 24—Single Vee.   Fig. 25—Double Vee.

sarily be the same, but it is most economical to have the bottom of both bevels at the center of the welded section.

(Note: These four terms are often interchanged, causing confusion and misunderstandings. The definitions given, with the accompanying sketches are standard in a large degree.)

Where to Use Bevel Types

As to the choice of bevels, the weldor should use either the double bevel or the double-V whenever possible, avoiding the other two types. The double bevel is satisfactory for material from $1/8$ to $1/2$ in. thick, and for $1/8$ in. or over the double-V. For the same thickness of material the amount of metal removed, and consequently the amount of space that must be filled, in the case of the double-V is only half that of the double bevel.

The dimensions of the bevel may vary with the thickness of the section, the method of welding, and the skill of the operator. Nothing is gained by making the opening wider than is necessary. The mistake most likely to occur, however, is making the angle so narrow that it does not permit free access to the bottom of the weld. When this happens, the weldor tries to dig through the pool to the bottom with the flame, and finally gets penetration at the cost of greatly overheating the metal. It is neither necessary nor desirable to bevel down to a sharp edge. A decidedly dull edge is better as it helps to preserve the alignment, and assists the operator in getting fusion at the bottom without melting a hole through.

The bevel may be machined, ground, chipped, or cut with the oxy-acetylene cutting torch. All methods are used in practice and give satisfactory results under different circumstances.

There is so much variety in production welding as well as repair welding that it would be useless to attempt to describe all of the uses for these many types of joints. In a good many cases the best choice is an obvious one after examining all of the different types. The selection as a general rule follows the principle of putting the weld metal where it will do the most good and if possible locating it where it will not have to stand unnecessary stresses, at the same time providing an opening which gives the weldor an opportunity to get thorough penetration.

After looking to the matter of design on a production job the next step is to determine whether or not a problem of expansion and contraction is involved and if so, to arrange a solution for this problem.

Expansion and Contraction

Practically all metals will expand when heated and contract again upon cooling. It is a perfectly natural property of the metals. The only difference in different metals being in the amount of expansion for given temperature rises. The expansion is in all directions, although it sometimes may appear to be most evident in one direction. There is also a difference in the rate at which different metals will conduct heat; so some metals will become heated over a greater area in a given time and consequently their distortion due to expansion will be noticeably different.

Opinions differ as to whether the distortion of metal shapes due to the welding operation should be blamed on expansion or contraction. However, it is common practice to deal chiefly with the subject of expansion because the expansion occurs first.

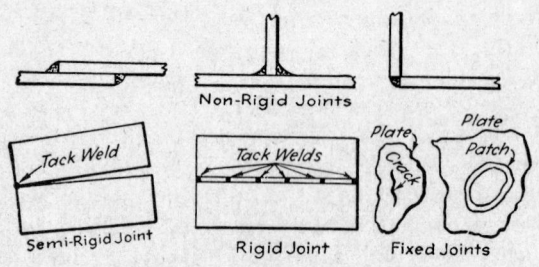

Fig. 26—Rigid and non-rigid welds.

Rigid and Non-Rigid Welds

There is one important fundamental fact concerning expansion which every weldor should thoroughly understand. That is, that this force cannot be eliminated. Expansion and contraction will follow the heating or cooling of metals, and there is no way to stop it. Sometimes it is possible to hold pieces together so rigidly for welding and during the cooling that there is no apparent indication of distortion when the work is completed. If, however, the weld is a rigid weld (Fig. 26), it is a certainty that under these conditions stresses have been set up by cooling inside the metal which greatly weaken it at the point or line of concentration of these stresses so that it will give way very readily. This is also true of a non-rigid weld. Such as in ordinary butt welding, in two lengths of pipe or the welding of two sheets. In all of these cases, the parts being free to move are drawn inward by the contraction stresses so that no interior stresses are left. Expansion effects can be so highly localized by using heavy plates next to the weld to conduct away the heat that they can be practically disregarded.

Heat Effect on Metal

The operator who is not familiar with the various indications of expansion and contraction will do well to perform a few simple experiments to see how these forces act. Lay a heavy bar or billet of iron or steel on a table with the position of the ends very accurately marked. Heat up some small area of the piece and note the amount of expansion. Let it cool, get the ends carefully in position again, and repeat the heating at another spot. It will be evident that the amount of expansion is dependent more on the absorption of heat than the location at which the heat is applied.

At Center of a Sheet

Now take a small, perfectly flat sheet, bring the center of it to a bright red heat over an area about the size of a silver dollar; allow it to cool and notice how it is warped. This warping is not altogether due to expansion and contraction. There were probably some stresses left in the metal when it was rolled and softening produced by the heat make it possible for these stresses to act and distort the metal.

Between Edges of Sheet

Next take two narrow strips of sheet metal about 12 inches long, place them edge to edge and start welding. Notice how the edges tend to expand at first but draw together as the weld progresses so that when the end of the seam is reached one sheet overlaps the other. Roll a piece of sheet metal in the form of a cylinder, hold the edges together by means of small tack welds and weld the longitudinal seam. Look at the end of the shell thus produced and notice that it is

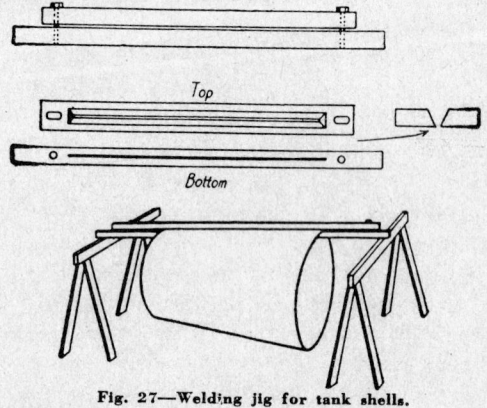

Fig. 27—Welding jig for tank shells.

not a perfect circle but that the shrinkage of the metal has distorted the section in the vicinity of the weld. These experiments will show some of the effects of expansion and contraction. Although these forces cannot be eliminated they can be controlled as far as the weldor is concerned, by making preparations to compensate for the action of these forces.

Tank Welding Preparation

One of the most important places where such preparation becomes necessary is in the welding of tanks.

The problem presented is the action noted above when two long strips were welded together. Some operators try to control these forces by tacking the seam together at short intervals so that the to edges of the seam are held rigidly in their respective position throughout the welding operation. This does not result in a neat job because although the seam is held open for the weldor, the forces actually twist the metal about so that a crooked seam results with the additional disadvantage, usually, of the shell being all out of shape.

A much better way to provide for expansion and contraction on sheet and plate work is to set up the work so that the edges almost touch at the end of the seam where the weld is started but gradually spread apart until there is a considerable separation at the far end of the seam. A rough rule for this preparation is to make the opening equal to the thickness of the metal multiplied by the length of the seam in feet. This rule is subject to a little variation in practice. Some weldors work faster than others and consequently do not use so much separation. When working on plate of $1/8$ in. thickness or more and on jobs where very particular work is desired, it is good practice to use some form of wedge clamp to hold the sheets in alignment, and to preserve the separation as the weld advances. It is also advisable to roll the sheets so that the section near the weld will be as near perfectly round as possible.

Welding Jig for Tank Shells

Even with these precautions it is very difficult to get a perfect seam on a long shell so where there is any considerable amount of such welding it is very economical to make jigs to hold the work (Fig. 27). tion when one edge only is beveled, but beveled from

The essential parts of such a jig are three in number. First, a heavy supporting section of iron, i.e., a heavy iron bar of sufficient length having a deep groove cut in and which will come directly under the lines of the weld. The second important piece of the equipment is a similar bar to go over the seam with a wide groove cut in and which will permit the weldor to reach the material to be welded with the flame. These

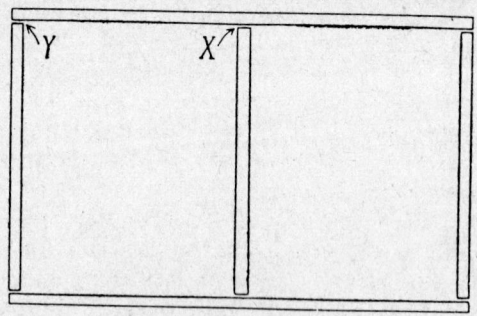

Fig. 28—Contraction effects.

two parts are hinged together at one end so as to cross over the work, and the third essential, a suitable clamp to hold it tightly during the welding operation. The sheet should be separated at the far end and the clamp should not be tightened so much that it will prevent the edges drawing together as the weld progresses.

A clamp or a jig of this type serves several useful purposes. It holds the metal rigidly in place for the weldor, it allows a more uniform rate of welding and consequently is a distinct aid to sound welding. It conducts heat away from the metal adjacent to the weld so that the forces of expansion and contraction are limited to a small area. Furthermore, the uniformity of the welding results in a very uniform distribution of heat, usually a much better looking job.

Preventives for Heat Effects

Not all welding operations on sheet and plate are as simple as the straight butt seam weld. Therefore, there are some which make the construction of jigs rather difficult. Jigs are always an economy when a great many welds of the same size and design are to be made. In cases where there are rather complicated designs and only a few welds to make, the effect of

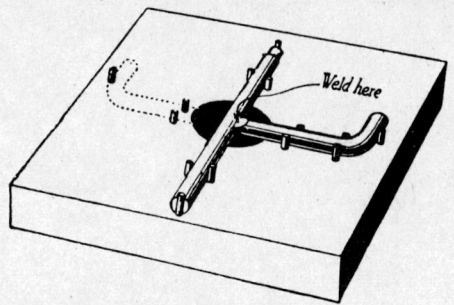

Fig. 29—Simple jig for welding tubing or rods.

expansion and contraction can be offset by deforming the material before welding in the direction opposite to the expected effect which the welding operation will have. In this case the final shrinkage will draw the pieces together in normal shape and position.

Another effect of contraction may be illustrated by reference to a sketch in Fig. 28. Suppose five pieces are to be joined as shown. If the outside corners are welded in succession, then the center piece welded in, the last weld being made at X, this will shrink upon cooling and draw the two long members inward. The shrinkage effect will be less noticeable if the inside members as well as the first and the final weld is made on one of the outside corners as at Y.

The type of jig used for making long seams takes

care of the contraction effect commonly called warping. On other types of welds, however, the same forces may act to draw pieces out of alignment. There are several types of jigs or holding devices which can be used to guard against this difficulty. For the welding together of pieces of tubing into different shapes, a jig can be constructed by welding sections of channel iron so

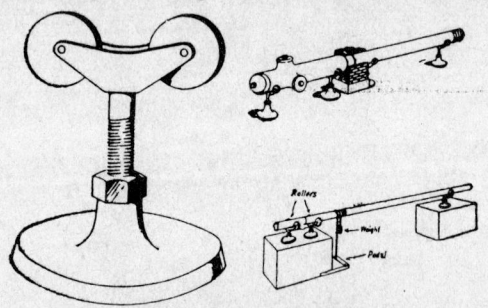

Fig. 30—Rollers for pipe welding.

as to produce a sort of mold in which the different lengths of tubing can be laid or clamped for welding.

Another device for this purpose is to use a piece of very heavy plate into which short rods or studs have been inserted in the right position to hold the parts properly (Fig. 29). When building a jig this way, it is advisable to cut holes in the plate directly below the location of the welds. An excellent jig for welding pipes can be made up of double rollers mounted on pedestals (Fig. 30). These can be clamped or bolted rigidly in position and the roller marked so that the weld can be made in the shortest possible time.

Preheating of Castings

It is in the repair welding of iron and aluminum castings that the weldor experiences his greatest difficulty with contraction. In this case the metal is so brittle that contraction stresses on rigid sections cause breaks to occur after the work has been completed. Fig. 31 is the diagram very commonly used to illustrate this principle. If a weld is made at "A" with all of the rest of the casting cooled there will be a break somewhere when its cools and contracts. However,

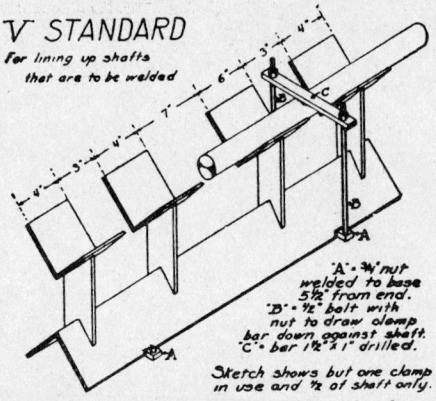

V STANDARD
For lining up shafts that are to be welded

"A" - ¾" nut welded to base 5½" from end.
"B" - ½" bolt with nut to draw clamp bar down against shaft.
"C" - bar 1½"x1" drilled.

Sketch shows but one clamp in use and ½ of shaft only.

A convenient jig for lining up shafts or tubes.

the break can be prevented by keeping the points "C" red hot while the weld at "A" is being made and allowing all three of the heated areas to cool together. This procedure is called preheating.

Preheating Devices

The procedure for preheating varies with each repair job. Sometimes it is local and sometimes the whole piece is preheated. There are cases when a preheating job must be done rapidly and in other cases plenty of time is allowed. Therefore, most shops are equipped with several types of preheating devices, using LP Gas, coke or charcoal. For such work as fly wheels and pulley wheels a concentrated local heat is required and is quickly secured with a blow torch burning city gas or oil. Local heat is more economical than general heat but it takes considerable experience for the weldor to learn how to use this method. A general heating, i.e., heating of the entire piece, may be accomplished by building a furnace of firebrick and using a charcoal fire. Charcoal burns with a hot flame, does not injure the metal and if the furnace is well constructed it requires no blast to keep it burning. The gradual heat which it produces prevents cracking and a piece preheated in this manner may be cooled slowly.

Charcoal Preheating

The first essential for a charcoal preheating oven is a good bottom. This can be made of fire brick and can be a permanent part of the floor. For the sake of the health of the operator care should be taken that the ventilation is good. In building up a wall of fire brick around the casting which is being preheated, allow plenty of space around the casting. Put a good layer of charcoal on the bottom and lay the casting on top of this, taking care to secure it in a position which will be as convenient as possible for the operator. Leave holes all the way around the bottom of the wall to provide draft. If the draft should prove too heavy it is an easy matter to close them. Make the wall of the furnace straight and solid. Lay a sheet or two of asbestos paper across the top, using some iron rods to support it if necessary. When the casting is ready to weld, a hole can be cut in the asbestos paper top large enough to allow access to the crack. It is also a good plan to punch a number of holes in the asbestos to provide an escape for the charcoal fumes.

As a general rule cast iron should be heated to a good red heat; aluminum, however, should not be heated over 800 F. When solder made of one-half tin and one-half lead will melt on an aluminum casting, the preheating has gone far enough. Aluminum loses its strength when it reaches high temperatures and an excess of preheating may cause a complete collapse

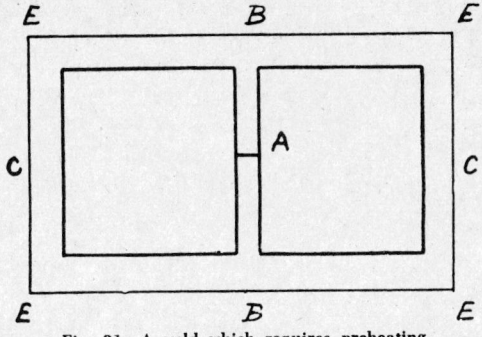

Fig. 31—A weld which requires preheating.

of the casting. For this reason may weldors prefer a preheating oven of the gas oven type for aluminum work. (See Pages 42–43.)

Maintaining Alignment

Expansion and contraction in cast iron welds may result in drawing the welded parts out of alignment in cases where there is no danger of breakage from contraction stresses. One of the most usual causes of loss of alignment in cast iron welds is placing tack welds on the top surface of the crack. The effect of this is to pull the parts out of place at once when the tack welds cool. This can be avoided by placing the tack welds on the ends of the crack instead of on the top. If parts of castings are tacked together before starting to weld the welding should not be started until after the tacks have cooled and the whole piece is examined for alignment. It is easy to maintain alignment if small contact areas are left when beveling out the crack in preparation for the welding.

Shape Welding Molds

Another piece of procedure which may come under the heading of preparation is the making of molds for shape welding. When worn surfaces are to be built up, or parts which have been knocked from a casting by accident, it takes little time to make a mold using carbon blocks, carbon plates or carbon paste,

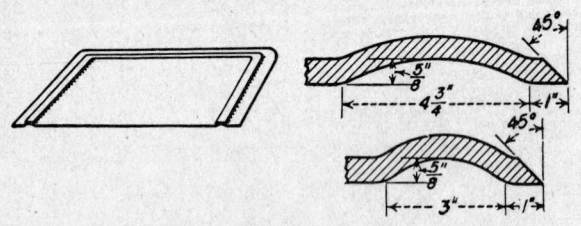

Fig. 32—Corrugated patch.

but the time saved in the welding operation and the practical certainty of getting a smooth and better job together with the time saved in machining the finished work will more than compensate for the trouble taken to complete the mold. Practically all welding supply dealers carry materials for this purpose.

Welding in a Patch

There is one type of repair in tank work which may give trouble if the proper preparation is not made, i.e., the welding in of a patch. If a flat piece of metal is used to make the patch and the welding does not extend to the edge of the plate at any point, the weldor will find that the patch will crack away from the rest of the plate when the weld cools. This can be prevented by using a dished patch which will absorb considerable heat from the welding and should be heated a little more toward the end of the work. While it cools a little hammering will simply flatten out the patch and there will be no cracking. Sometimes a corrugated patch (Fig. 32) is used instead of a dished patch.

Clean Metal Is Important

A discussion of preparation for welding would not be complete without mentioning the importance of working on clean metal whenever possible. Cleaning can be done with a sand blast, grinder or wire brush. This should always be done as thoroughly as circumstances will permit. Avoid welding on the surfaces which are covered with rust, scale, paint, dirt or grease. Weldors accustomed to working altogether with steel learn how to work slag out of the weld, and are apt to depend on this ability too much when they encounter other metals. It is unwise to count on puddling out impurities in such operations as brazing, silver brazing and hard facing, where clean surfaces are an extremely important consideration.

Economy of Good Preparation

There is one big advantage in preparing a weld properly, i.e., that it greatly reduces the time and materials necessary to making the welds and also reduces the chances of failure. There is more danger of losing time on account of poor preparation than there is of wasting time in the preparation itself.

CHAPTER 7
INSPECTING THE WELD

There is considerable difference of opinion among people who use oxy-acetylene welding regarding average quality of the completed work. Some experienced supervisors are able to keep their men turning out work of such high quality that they look upon a thoroughly sound weld (Figs. 1 and 2) as being easy to obtain. There are others, who do not understand all the fundamentals of welding, who get a very poor quality job and think that they are doing about as well as can be done. The operator who is anxious to make progress in the art of welding can find nothing which will help him more than the ability to inspect his work and pick out the more common faults. This chapter will be devoted to a discussion of a number of types of defective welds, the causes of the difficulties, and the methods of overcoming them.*

Lack of Penetration

Probably the most common fault of unskilled weldors is the lack of penetration (Figs. 3 and 4). This term is sometimes misunderstood by the weldor. He may observe that molten metal is dropping from the bottom side of the joint on which he is working and come to the conclusion that he is getting full penetration. There are several possibilities in being wrong in this conclusion. In the first place, this penetration may be spotty, i.e., complete part of the way with other

*Most of the illustrations of sectional views in this chapter were obtained by etching the sections with etching acid after cutting. Etching brings out the different parts of the section, which cannot usually be seen on unetched sections because of the saw marks.

portions not welded all the way through. He may also be mislead by seeing the flame go all the way through when the weld itself does not get to the bottom. Another possibility is that the molten metal may be separated from the faces of the bevel by a film of oxide. The important point of penetration is that we take it to mean that the fusing process has penetrated

Fig. 1—Longitudinal sections of sound weld, good fusion and thorough penetration.

entirely through both edges of the parts to be joined so that the portion which is effected by the welding is just as solid all the way through as the adjacent parent metal.

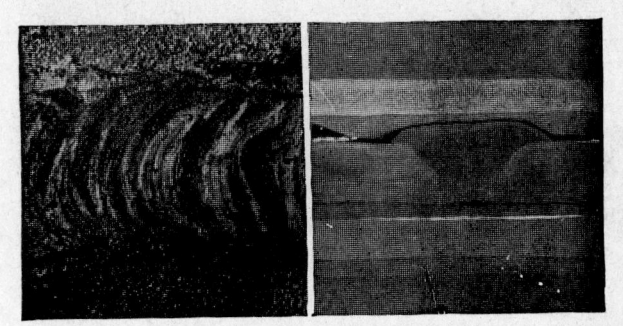

Fig. 2—Top and section of sound weld.

This result can only be obtained when sufficient opening is provided to allow starting the weld from the bottom and when the welding is started from the bottom and carried to the top. There is probably no other fault so common among poor weldors as the failure to get full penetration. This fault should be avoided because if the welded part is subjected to bending, a poorly penetrated weld is already weakened part way through and will consequently not stand as much as the parent metal does. If the weld is subjected

Fig. 3—Inside of a weld poorly penetrated.

to tensile stress (pulling) the force will all be concentrated in a small area with the result that there will be a break in the weld just as in bending. An inspection of the reverse side of a weld will very often show whether the parts have been fused all the way

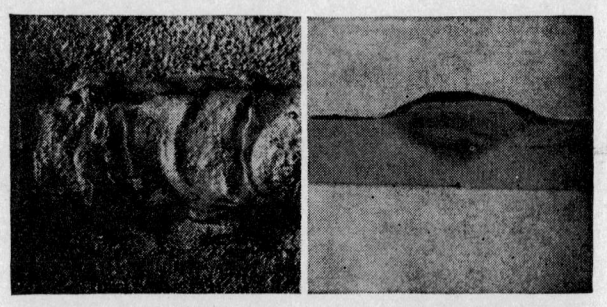

Fig. 4—Top and section of poorly penetrated weld.

through. The weldor can easily check his own ability to get penetration by welding a couple of sample pieces, following his habitual procedure, then cutting them across the weld and observing the appearance of the deposit.

Poor Fusion

Another common difficulty found in beginners' welds is poor fusion (Figs. 5 and 6). This may be entirely independent of the penetration. Good fusion consists in handling the molten metal so that clean sound metal is deposited throughout the weld. Some of the indications of poor fusion are laminations, adhesions,

Fig. 5—Inside of a weld poorly fused.

slag inclusions and oxide inclusions. *Laminations* occur in the weld when successive layers of molten metal are deposited in the bevel without taking care to fuse each new layer thoroughly with the layer below it and float out all of the slag and oxides. This may

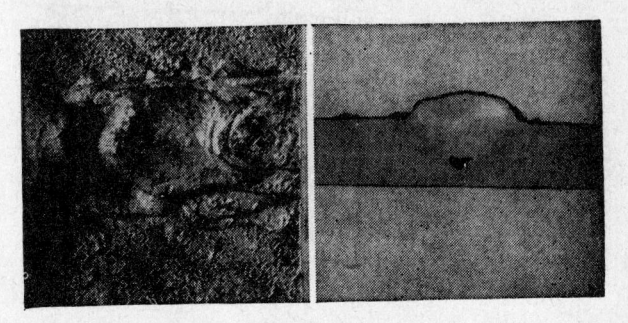

Fig. 6—Top and section of poorly fused weld.

give quite a volume of good sound metal in the bevel but if it is made up of many layers or drops of metal which are not thoroughly fused together, the side will have very little strength. This difficulty is easily recognized when such a weld is broken and the appearance of the fracture is compared with the appearance of a fracture in the parent metal. *Adhesions* are obtained when the molten metal, or puddle, is allowed to flow ahead along the face of the bevel, before these faces are sufficiently melted to unite in fusion with the deposited metal. It is possible to make a very pretty weld in this manner and one which will

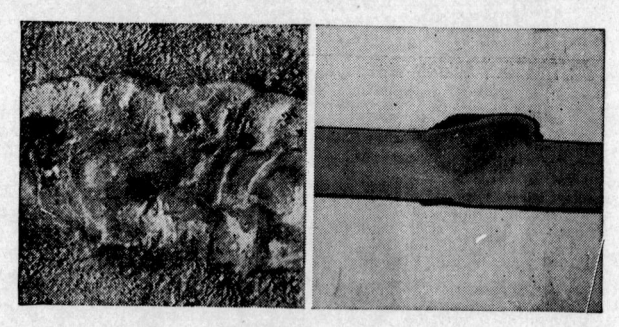

Fig. 7—Weld undercut on one side.

have a fairly good quality of deposited metal, but the joint will be poor because the deposited metal is not fused to the parent metal. *Slag inclusions* result from welding on dirty metal or with dirty filler rod, and not taking care to work all the slag to the top of the pool where it can do no harm. When slag particles are included in the weld metal, they weaken it just as worm holes weaken a piece of wood. *Oxide inclusions*, of course result from failure to work all of the oxides to the top of the pool and they have the same effect as slag inclusions. These inclusions can only be detected by examining the interior of the weld metal. If this is found to be dirty, it is safe to assume that the dirty portions are inclusions of one sort or the other. Poor fusion is another way of saying poor welding and a weld which shows any of these characteristics is not properly made. This difficulty can be avoided by following the instructions for manipulation of the torch and welding rod.

Under-cut Weld

In the welding of long seams the beginner is apt to make the mistake known as under-cutting (Figs. 7

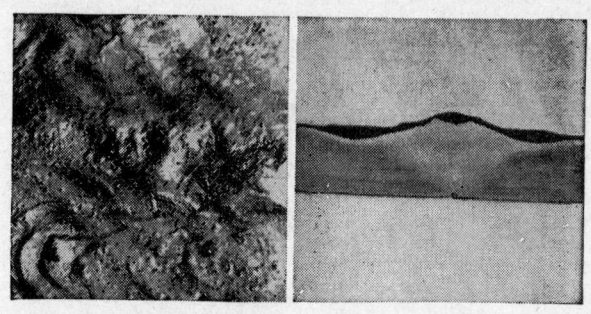

Fig. 8—Weld undercut on both sides.

and 8). This means that while the weld itself may be perfectly made, the heat of flame has been improperly manipulated so that portions of the parent metal alongside the weld will melt away, reducing the thickness of the parent metal at that point. Every weldor should watch his work and be sure that he does not leave any undercut spots on either side of the seam. There is no danger of this if he devotes the proper amount of skill in applying the heat evenly.

Incipient Crack

The fault known as an incipient crack is also one which occurs in learning to weld long seams. This may be caused simply by failure to get complete penetration, i.e., the penetration may be so complete that it appears to be 100 per cent, but the bottom part may consist of a thin layer of oxide which has no strength and consequently makes an opening when any stress is applied to the weld (Fig. 9). Another cause of incipient cracks is poor alignment of the sheets before the welding is started. If they are slightly out of line, it is practically impossible to weld from the top in such a way as not to leave an incipient

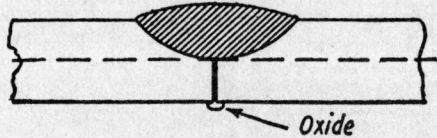

Fig. 9—Oxide at bottom of weld.

crack at the bottom (Fig. 10). In fact, although the work may be lined up at the start, the provision for overcoming expansion and contraction may be at fault,

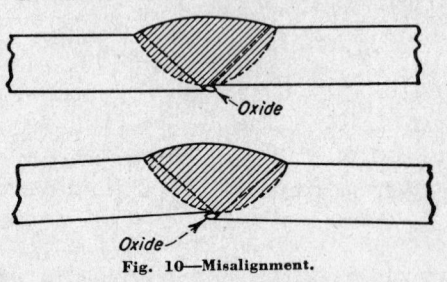

Fig. 10—Misalignment.

with the result that one of the lower edges of the weld pulls up over the other, throwing the plates out of alignment and resulting in incipient cracks. One way to guard against this difficulty is to leave about $1/16$ in. (or in heavy sections $1/8$ in.) when beveling the parts. This makes it easy to get perfect alignment and also to maintain the alignment. Care must be taken, however, to work the oxides to the top, so they will not coat the bottom edges and cause adhesions, which appear well to the inexpert eye, but are not thoroughly fused (Fig. 11). Another precaution against this difficulty consists in running a light weld on the reverse side, but care must be taken to make sure that this second weld penetrates all the way through to the first and joins with it so as not to leave an unwelded area inside.

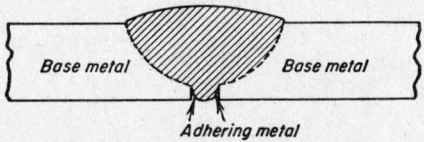

Fig. 11—Oxide films cause adhesions.

A welded structure which is full of wrinkles and buckled areas is evidence of poor workmanship. Tanks, tubing, metal furniture, door and window casings, and

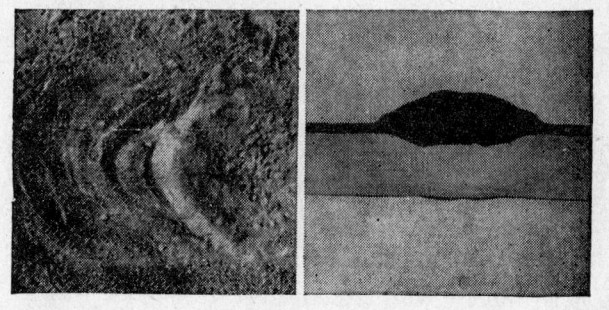

Fig. 12—Shallow spot.

similar products are turned out in enormous quantities daily, without evidence of warping. Some of the finest automobile body work is oxy-acetylene welded also. This is evidence enough that warping can be avoided. Usually this fault is due to a poor set-up which does not provide for expansion and contraction of the metal. If the set-up is correct for the work, warping may be caused by welding too slowly which allows too much time for the heat to be conducted back into the sheet. It may also be caused by using too large a tip in an attempt to get more speed.

Shallow spots in the weld (Fig. 12), indicating

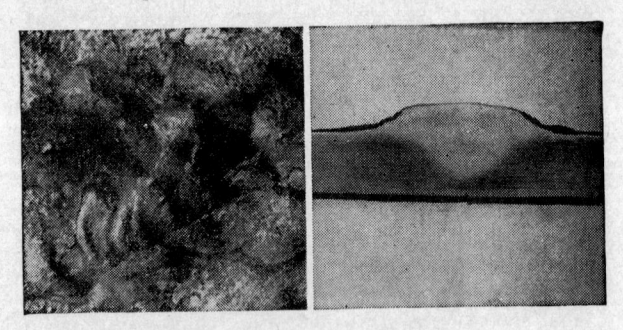

Fig. 13—Too much reinforcement.

an insufficient deposit of filler material in the bevel, furnish clear evidence of careless operation. It may seem unnecessary to mention such an obvious defect, but this is a point which the supervisor of production welding always has to watch if he is not sure of his men. It can usually be corrected by impressing upon the operator the need of thoroughness in making each joint.

In direct contrast to shallowness is the defect of making too much reinforcement (Fig. 13). This can be checked quite accurately by using a metal gauge (Fig. 14), machined out to fit over the weld and show whether the deposit comes inside the maximum and minimum requirements. The inexperienced weldor may try to compensate for lack of penetration by over-reinforcement (Fig. 15), and should be shown that, in the first place he makes the weld weaker instead of stronger by over-reinforcement, and in the second place he wastes time, gas and material.

Stiffness in a weld may or may not be desirable. It may cause the welded structure to break outside the weld in case of extraordinary stress, when no break would have occurred if the weld had been so made as

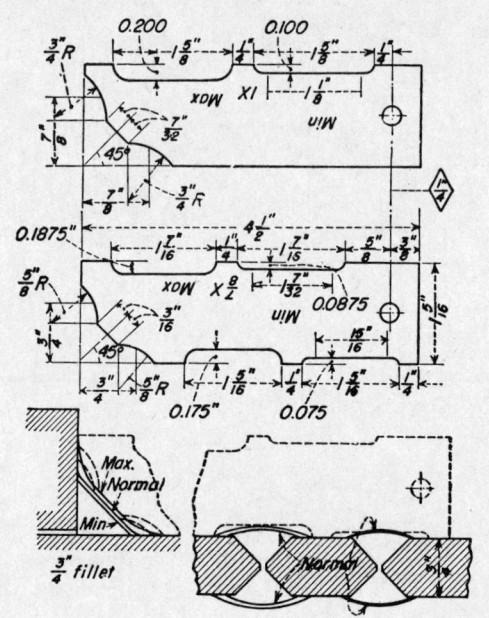

Fig. 14—Weld gauge for butt and fillet welds.

to be as ductile as the rest of the structure. Stiffness which is secured by applying a reinforcement so that it rises sharply at right angles to the parent metal, instead of sloping gradually from it, is an undesirable quality, because it forms a perfect line of leverage where a progressive fracture can start.

Oxidized Weld

Oxidized metal (Fig. 16) is brittle and weak and must be carefully avoided on important work. It is caused by welding with an oxidizing flame. This is not to be confused with occasional oxides which may be present in any weld puddle made with a correctly adjusted flame and only need to be floated or worked to the surface. If the weldor is not able to keep his flame adjusted continually to neutral, a careful inspection should be made of the regulators and the torch

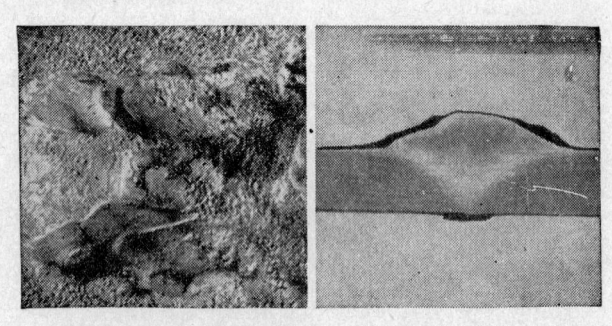

Fig. 15—Over reinforcement with incomplete penetration.

Hard Spots

Hard spots are not at first easy to detect by visual examination, and, in fact, may be present below the surface, but they become evident when the weld is machined, or when they become the starting points of progressive fractures. Sometimes, however, they show up on the surface as whitened areas. Hard spots are common defects of cast iron welds. They are caused by sudden cooling or chilling of the molten metal. When the chilling is rapid, the carbon in the casting does not have time to separate from the iron in graphitic form, but is held in solution and frozen, producing an iron carbide which is very hard. But it is not enough to leave this subject with so general an explanation of the cause. Hard spots are usually undesirable, and the several methods of chilling which produce them should be studied and avoided. Introducing a cold welding rod into the puddle is one way to produce them. Surface hard spots may be formed by going over the top of the weld after it has cooled and remelting small high areas, which become chilled by the cold metal beneath. Hardened areas in the weld

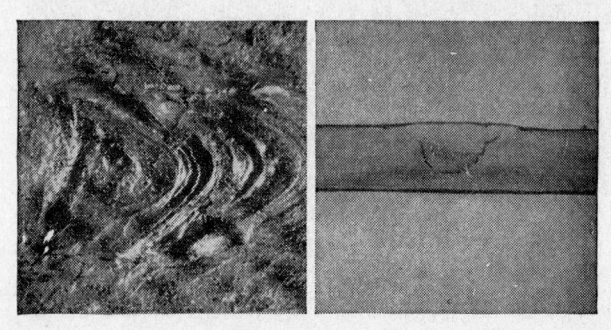

Fig. 16—Weld made with oxidizing flame.

itself are caused by not having the adjacent metal hot enough to prevent this chilling. Therefore the adjacent metal must be kept hot and a large puddle maintained, then the back part of the puddle must be allowed to solidify slowly as the weld advances. It is evident that the ripple welding procedure is less apt to cause hard spots than the method of successive puddles. Slow cooling of the whole piece is necessary.

Blowholes in Welds

Another defect in poorly made cast iron welds is the presence of blowholes. Often they can be seen plainly in the top of the weld, which may generally

126   INSPECTING THE WELD

be taken as an indication that blowholes are also present in the body of the weld as well. Blowholes may be formed by gasifying particles of foreign matter in the parent metal or filler rod, or by the method of welding. The use of too small a puddle, with insufficient heating of the adjacent metal, and playing the flame directly into the puddle will not only produce

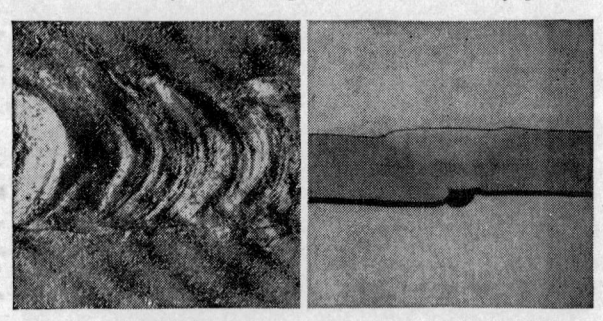

Fig. 17—Weld made with carburizing flame.

these holes, but may force them down into the weld. The parent metal must be well heated near the weld, and the puddle kept large and hot, with the flame slanted ahead so that it does not impinge upon the back part of the puddle when it is solidifying. As a

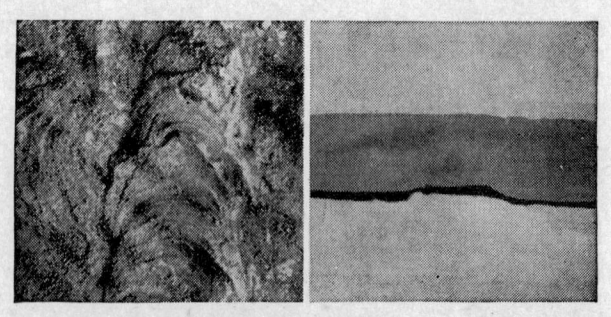

Fig. 18—Good crossover.

rule the weldor can avoid blowholes by watching for them in the puddle and floating them out, that is, making the puddle so large and hot that the metal under the hole becomes liquid and the hole comes to the top and disappears.

Carburized Welds

Carburized weld metal in steel welds tends to make them somewhat brittle. It is caused, of course, by using a carburizing flame instead of a neutral flame (Fig. 17). The general appearance of a carburized weld is somewhat different from a good weld, showing

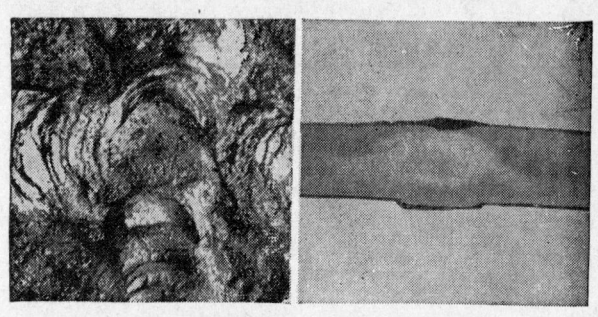

Fig. 19—Poor crossover.

small holes and radial lines from the center toward the outside of the ripples. If this fault is suspected the weldor should try a small weld after adjusting his flame to make it carburizing, and note the bubbling and sparkling. He will then recognize this indication of a carburizing flame when doing real work, and be prepared to correct it by making the proper flame adjustment.

Common Defects

A fault on which beginners should be checked is failure to weld through tacks which have been made in plates or pipes to hold them in position for welding. Often this can only be detected by cutting through the weld where it crosses a tack weld. A similar defect frequently is encountered where one line of weld crosses over another (Figs. 18 and 19).

A more obvious defect is failure to keep the weld full size when finishing at the end of a seam, leaving

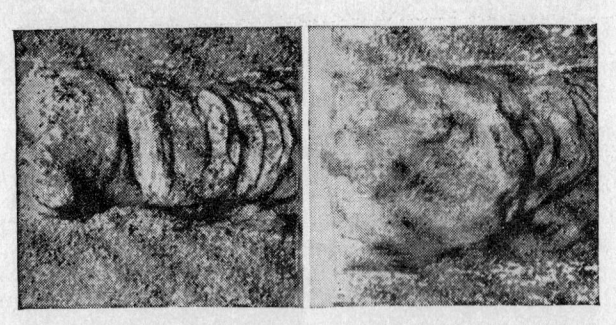

Fig. 20—Good ending of seam.
Fig. 21—Poor ending of seam.

a cup or pocket at this point (Figs. 20 and 21). A little practice in manipulating the pool of molten metal will overcome this. Another place to check is where the weldor has stopped, allowed the metal to solidify, and started again. A skillful operator can stop and start without leaving evidence of the interruption.

Practically all of these defects are deviations from the original definition of welding given in this volume. In the title of this chapter the word "inspection" has been used to signify an examination of the weld for its quality. A later chapter will cover the subject of testing. There the purpose will be to determine whether the completed weld will, regardless of defects, stand up under the service for which it is intended. As far as the faults mentioned in this chapter are concerned, they must all be avoided if a perfect weld is to be secured. Therefore, frequent reference should be made to the above discussion when checking the results of the beginners' exercises.

Sparks can be a fire hazard in flame cutting.

CHAPTER 8
LEARNING TO WELD

Training of operators is a subject which may range all the way from breaking in a helper in a small shop doing general repair work to arranging a complete systematic course of welding instruction for a large crew to weld on a pipe line hundreds of miles long. In either case or in any of the intermediate cases the subject can be treated at great lenghts or summed up in a few paragraphs.

Fundamentals are Important

Many welding shops consider that it takes several years to train a new man to handle their complete range of work, while in some production welding departments weldors who have had only a few hours of instruction are doing satisfactory work. This accounts for the great differences of opinion which exist on this subject. The information given in this volume is what is considered essential for every man who works with the oxy-acetylene torch. In the present chapter it will deal with the important points involved in training, the object being to help new men understand what they are doing and why they are doing it.

Selecting the Individual

The selection of men for training, based upon their natural qualifications for the work to be done, is really the first problem presented. No general physical qualification exists. On some types of fine light work, girls and women do excellent welding, in fact they may do better than men or boys. On other classes of work the physical characteristics of the job are so strenuous that only the strongest can stand the pressure. A weldor with long experience in a repair shop where every weld is made with exacting care so that a second break will not occur in the same place, will often grow weary of the dull routine of production welding, and find it especially hard to work continuously without rest between jobs. The production weldor, on the other hand, finds it awkward to set up his own work and figure out his own procedure for doing each new task if he is set at work in the repair shop, and finds the requirements of the weld very burdensome. Usually the skilled repair weldor shows signs of better training than the production weldor, unless the latter has had general training in the process. The former has been trained to weld, and the latter to perform a welding operation.

Qualities to Consider

Weldors, therefore, may not be chosen on the basis of physique, or previous welding experience. Yet there are principles which will help in making a selection. First of all, consider the apparent mental attitude of the candidate. Some welds may fail without causing trouble, but not many. Welds are expected to hold the stress which the parent metal will hold, and it is quite well known that welds can be made to do that. A workman who does not seem to be the sort who will take pride in his work, will not take pains without being watched, will not respond correctly to suggestions, is not a good candidate for a welding job. Good workmanship is scarcely possible without a certain amount of job pride.

A sober man is much to be desired, because his hand is steady every day of the week. On anything except the simplest straight seam welding, a man who is clever with his hands is a distinct asset. On simple work for which good set-ups are provided, a steady, solid type is easily trained to turn out remarkably good welds at a very uniform rate. Girls and women are preferred in a number of factories on very light sheet and tube welding.

The roaming adventurer type of man gets along best on pipe line work, where the living conditions are often close to primitive. Welding all day on heavy sections or in boilers takes a man with a strong constitution. Ability along mechanical lines is an asset to a weldor on any kind of work.

Exact Schedule Needed

As to the training program, regardless of how many weldors are to be employed, each shop should have a definite written schedule of instruction. This schedule should cover as much detail as possible concerning the apparatus and materials used in welding, the care of apparatus, methods of economizing materials, and safety precautions. All of these are important from an economy standpoint.

Know a Good Weld

The weldor should be taught what a weld is, and the full significance of fusion. He should be shown just what the weld is for, and what constitutes a good weld. Good welds and imperfect welds should be carefully compared for his benefit and while he practices, the causes of weld defects should be explained, together with the corrective measures. He should be made to realize that he becomes a real weldor by learning how to fuse metals properly, rather than by simply making welds which will pass an inspector in the shop. A good sound weld having a rough finish on top, tested alongside a half fused weld with a fine looking finish, will demonstrate how it is possible to make a good weld which will not pass inspection.

Teach Proper Attitude

If the beginner learns to think of his weld first and the inspection second, he will eventually develop into a dependable workman, but if he measures success in terms of passing inspection, he will always require watching, and the fault will be that of the instructor. Men trained along these lines go readily from one type of welding to another and therefore have greater earning power. The employer also benefits from a lower welding cost, because the supervisor is relieved of a great deal of unnecessary detail work and can give his attention almost entirely to general improvement.

Ground Work is Vital

The shop work involved in training operators is often at fault with respect to the amount of attention given to fundamentals. Too often there is a desire to put all beginners through in a definite number of periods. This is all right if men are dropped from the course as soon as it becomes apparent that they cannot keep up with the others. The mistake lies in forcing them ahead before they have mastered preliminary work. A beginner should be kept on an exercise until he can do it correctly. He will learn more from fewer exercises if he learns everything thoroughly as he goes along.

The preliminary part of the weldor's training is without doubt the most vital part of it, because the care expended in teaching the fundamentals of good practice is more important than the number of hours spent in shop exercises.

Some employers prefer to hire men who have had experience with the torch, rather than use the time and gas required to train them, but by training men properly it is possible to save a great deal more than the training costs. In fact, the cost of gases and materials for instruction purposes should not be very high. Control of the molten metal can be learned to a large extent with a small flame and thin metal, and control of the metal is the chief aim of the training. The habit of the correct motion of the rod and torch can be learned just about as fast by doing a lot of practicing with an unlighted torch. When the beginner does not have to actually watch the flame and the metal he will unconsciously learn a lot about making himself comfortable for his work. It is a good thing to learn at this stage that comfort is conducive to steady,

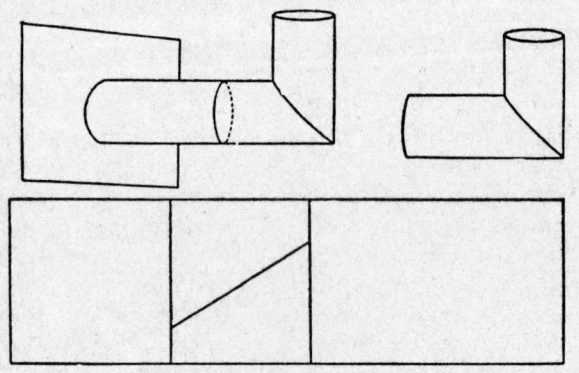

Fig. 1—Shop exercise for sheet metal weldors.

uninterrupted operation, which will result in more and better welding in a day.

Assuming that at least five 2-hour periods are available for preliminary instruction, a good program could be laid out as follows:

First Period of Instruction

Demonstration of short simple weld by instructor, with explanation that the same principles of getting a good union apply uniformily to all welds. Explanation of just what has taken place in making the weld. Ten minutes of this is enough to satisfy a student's impatience to see the actual work.

If the instructor takes pains to name all the parts of the equipment and use welding words and terms freely, the student is impressed with the necessity of learning the meaning of these words and will attend more willingly to the instruction which immediately follows. The outfit can then be taken apart, and each part of it can be explained carefully, with special reference to the uses of each part, and the function of each gas.

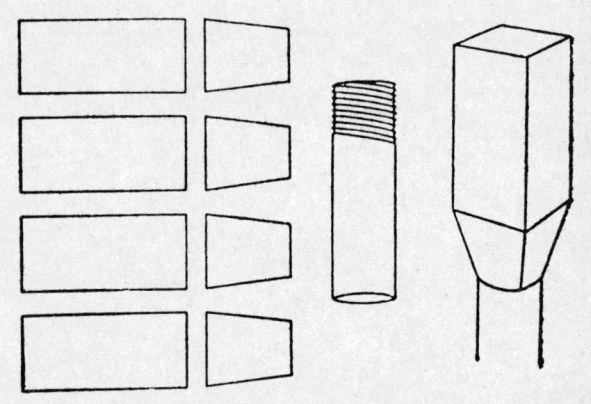

Fig. 2—Shop exercise for tank weldors.

Then have the student assemble the outfit, light the torch and fuse together a couple of flanged one-inch squares of sheet metal, then take the outfit apart. This takes more time in case there are several in a class, because each motion will have to be checked on each man. The remaining time can be spent in a discussion of the various parts of the equipment, emphasis at this time being placed on care of the apparatus and safety precautions.

The Second Period

Start by letting student ask questions regarding things which are not clear from the first period. If the student does not ask questions the instructor should ask enough to satisfy himself that the work of the first period has been fairly well remembered. Then go through the procedure of assembling the apparatus up to the adjustment of the neutral flame, shut off the flame, take the apparatus apart, and note the time taken. Repeat this exercise two or three times, making note always of how long it takes, and taking the opportunity to review the discussion about the apparatus.

In the last half of the period let the student melt metal with neutral, carburizing, and oxidizing flames until he can tell from the action of the metal what flame adjustment has been made by the instructor. The reason for this is that the weldor must give his attention to the pool when he is welding and if for any reason the flame adjustment changes he should recognize it at once by the action of the metal. At the end of the period he should disassemble the outfit and pack it away.

The Third Period

Show the student by simple diagrams the importance of fusion and penetration. It is an excellent plan to have samples of several types of welds, both good and bad, for comparison, and demonstrate the causes of apparent defects, and the correct procedure for avoiding them.

Have the student set up a simple weld, assemble his equipment, and make the weld. Then have him compare it with the sample and form his own opinion of it first, in advance of any criticism by the instructor. A weldor who can make an honest and intelligent criticism of his own workmanship will never cease to make progress. Point out any defects which he has not noticed, and repeat the exercise until real progress is made. Put away the apparatus and use the remaining time in discussion of questions suggested by the student's performance.

The Fourth Period

Have student set up apparatus and set up work for same exercise used in previous period. Try working with too large a tip, and too small a tip, and, if filler rod is used, with too large and too small filler rods, in combination with correct and incorrect tip sizes. Use extremes at first so that the effect will be more noticeable. Take plenty of time to discuss various weld defects which develop. At the end of the period have student try the same exercise with all conditions correct and compare the result with his best work of the previous period. Let the student be his own critic as far as possible.

The Fifth Period

A short talk, using illustrations or demonstrations if possible, on beveling, expansion, cleaning the parent metal, etc., to prepare the student for more extended discussions. Then have an exercise prepared which will be similar to the type of work he is expected to do. For example:

If the work is to be all straight corner seams, a two-foot seam of this type will do.

If the work is to be all straight butt seams, a two-foot butt seam will do.

If the work is to be on flanged joints a two-foot joint of this type will do.

If the standard procedure is to tack before welding the student should include the tacking in this exercise.

For a shop where general sheet metal welding is done a more elaborate job may be undertaken. A long sheet can be cut so as to provide three pieces which can be rolled into cylindrical shapes, two of them being mitred, and leaving a fourth piece flat. The mitered pieces can be welded together to form an elbow, this elbow welded onto the straight cylinder, and the latter to the flat piece (Fig. 1). Such an exercise convinces the student of the need for study of the principles involved, and can be repeated at the end of the entire course as a general test of efficiency.

If the shop work is to be thick plate, a 12 in. weld on boiler plate will be enough for this exercise.

If the shop work is building up instead of joining seams or cracks, building up exercises should be arranged both with and without molds.

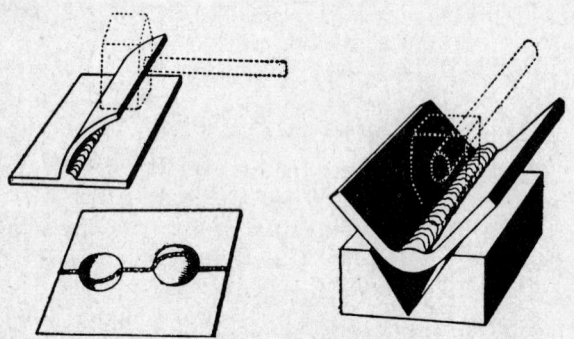

Fig. 3—Tests of shop exercise.

For pipe weldors, a butt joint in 3 in. pipe, followed by a 3 in. tee weld, makes a good exercise.

For tank weldors the nine small pieces shown in Fig. 2 may be welded to the form shown, and the miniature tank which results may be welded to the end of a small piece of half-inch pipe so that it may be tested. This may also be used as a test at the end of a complete course, or as a proficiency test at any time.

A few tests of shop exercises are shown in Fig. 3.

These five period programs are not offered as a complete welding course. They merely suggest a careful method of getting at the fundamentals in the early part of the course, so that the rest of the instruction may proceed faster and with greater benefit to the student. Not much actual welding is involved, but what there is of it has a definite and necessary fundamental purpose. All weld failures are directly traceable to fundamental errors.

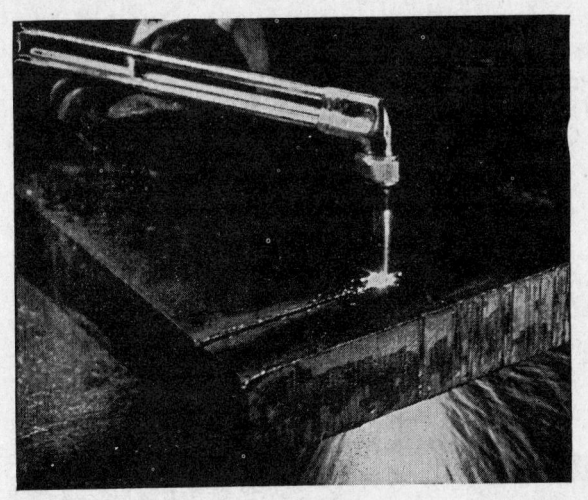

Skillful flame cutting quickly produces clean, smooth edges.

CHAPTER 9
WELDING PROPERTIES OF COMMON METALS

The emphasis placed upon steel and steel welding in previous chapters does not mean that steel is the only metal which can be welded or that it is necessarily the most difficult. Steel has been chosen as a basis for discussion because of the great volume of production welding of this metal. Many of the fundamental principles explained before will apply equally to other metals and their alloys. The present chapter will discuss the characteristics of irons and steels, with special reference to weldability and special methods of welding, and also the non-ferrous metals and alloys. Opinions differ as to what metal is easiest to weld, and these opinions are often dependent upon the quality of weld itself.

Cast Iron

Cast iron is one of the most interesting metals to the repair weldor. Poured molten into molds, it is used to make a wide variety of machinery parts in all shapes and sizes. Of the commercial varieties, gray cast iron contains from 3 to 4% carbon of which aproximately 1% is combined and the remainder in the free or graphite state. Tensile strength is comparatively low, but it will withstand about 80,000 psi compression. It is soft and easily machined. White cast iron, on the other hand, is produced by rapid chilling when the molten metal is poured into the mold. More of the carbon combines with the metal and less remains in the free or graphitic state. It is extremely hard and difficult to machine. The two are not difficult to distinguish, since gray cast iron makes a clean break. It can also be identified by use of an emery wheel. The sparks given off are small and red and a few will tend to explode or sparkle.

Reaction When Molten

It is well for the weldor first undertaking work on this metal to note its reaction under the welding flame. A formation of scum will appear on the surface of the liquid metal which is easily dissolved by use of a little cast iron flux. Usually the flux is applied by dipping the hot end of the filler rod into a can of flux before introducing it into the puddle. Another point that will be noted is that cast iron passes quickly from the solid state to a liquid state when sufficiently heated, instead of passing through a plastic state which occurs when steel is subjected to heat. Melting points of various grades will vary, but 2200 F may be accepted as a general figure.

Preparing for Welding

When a broken casting comes in for repair the first consideration in preparing it for welding is to thoroughly clean it of grease, sand, scale, rust or any foreign matter. If there are several broken pieces, they should be carefully matched and lined up. A good bevel should be cut along the line of break either by chipping, grinding or cutting. If the torch is used, the surface should be ground or thoroughly sand blasted.

Preheating the Casting

If the casting is of sufficient size or such complex structure that preheating is required, it should be laid on a bed of fire brick (it is well to have such a bed built into the shop floor rather than lay brick on top of cement) with bricks under any sections that require support. Build up several courses of fire brick around the casting or until slightly higher than the top. The first course should have several openings which are used to control the draft. Start a slow fire on the bed with a few pieces of charcoal, gradually adding more while a preliminary soaking heat is put into the piece. *Never start a full fire at once,* for distortion is sure to develop further breaks. When the casting is thoroughly soaked, more charcoal can be added and the furnace covered with asbestos paper. It is left thus until the part develops a dark red color—visible in a darkened room—particularly at the break and surrounding areas. In some cases the structure of the casting requires that the entire piece be brought to an even uniform temperature.

Welding Technique

Welding may now be started. It is suggested for preheated jobs that a hole just large enough to work through be made in the asbestos, so that the casting will not be subjected to chilling drafts. The flame should be applied clear to the bottom of the vee, working from side to side so that both sections are completely melted and a good sized pool of molten metal maintained. When filler metal is added *never* introduce a cold rod into the puddle. The proper method is to hold it in the envelope of the flame until it is heated almost to the melting point. Hard spots in the weld will develop if this correct procedure is not followed. From time to time as oxides and foreign matter work to the surface of the puddle, the welding rod should be dipped into the flux can and added to the weld. Continual puddling with the flame and the rod will dissolve the oxides and work foreign matter to the surface.

The welding rod recommended should be the best obtainable and contain a generous amount of silicon. On large jobs, it is sometimes possible to weld several lengths together in a bundle, so that the rate of deposition can be speeded up. The flux used should also be of good quality and should be used as needed. Never attempt to weld cast iron without it. It is well on large jobs if two men are available so that one can relieve the other. To stop and restart a job may result in blow holes. When the weld is nearing completion, it may be advisable to build up bosses or reinforcement at the point of break to give added strength to the repaired part, so that a second failure will not occur at the same point.

Post Heating Castings

After the weld is completed sufficient charcoal should be added to bring the part up to a uniform heat. It is then covered with asbestos, the fire allowed to die out by itself. The casting should *not* be removed until it is stone cold. This procedure practically amounts to a heat-treatment and castings so handled are often superior to those delivered from foundry molds.

Bronze Welding Cast Iron

Under many circumstances it is practical to use the bronze welding process to repair breaks in cast iron. The technique has been highly perfected and has proved very useful. The advantages are that comparatively little heat is needed, frequently little or no preheating is required so that time for dismantling is saved, and bronze welds if properly made are extremely strong.

Preparing the Joint

When welding with bronze it is necessary to make a good bevel and thoroughly clean the metal on both sides. This cleaning should not be done by grinding or machining alone, but should preferably be followed by sand blasting which is the best method of preparation for a bronze weld. Another good idea, lacking facilities for sand blasting, is to go over the surface of the fracture rapidly with a hot oxy-acetylene flame. The reason for either sand blasting or the application of the flame is to remove particles of free carbon in the metal which will prevent a good bond between the cast iron and the bronze.

A tip of the proper size should be selected and should be large enough so that the flame will not have to be applied too long in one place and cause overheating. Overheating will not only prevent a good union between the bronze and the parent metal, but it will usually result in burning out some of the important elements of the bronze. The parent metal itself should not be heated above a red heat.

A good welding position is that of back hand welding on steel. There is also considerable advantage in setting up the work so that the weld proceeds in an uphill direction. This makes it possible to get full penetration without overheating and greatly reduces the amount of surface which it is necessary to keep tinned ahead of the weld.

Torch Technique

With the work properly set up, begin heating the metal, seeing that the flame plays over both sections evenly. As the heating progresses the bronze rod should be held in the envelop of the flame and just as the cast iron approaches red the rod should be dipped into the flux. When a good red heat appears on the surface, the rod is introduced into the weld and applied to both sides of the break. If the right temperature is maintained the bronze will immediately spread over the surface of the weld in a thin layer, this action is called tinning. The rest of the weld is built up on this tinning layer. Best practice is to build up the weld in one pass on long seams. Care must be exercised to see that proper tinning proceeds in advance of building up the complete deposit.

Work only on clean metal, avoid overheating, refrain from going back over any welded portion to smooth it up and always use good flux prepared specially for this type of work and good bronze rods.

Test of Technique

A good test of technique is to take a small piece of scrap cast iron and build up a boss about ½ in. in diameter and about 1 in. high. When it has cooled, knock this boss off with a heavy hammer. If it leaves the casting cleanly, it was not properly applied. If it causes a fracture in the boss itself, the correct procedure was not used, but if it breaks so that the welded boss remains solid, and tears out some of the cast iron with it, the technique is correct. A bronze weld in cast iron should be stronger than the casting.

Malleable Iron

A great many small malleable iron castings find their way to the repair welding shop. These often show signs of having been broken easily and the weldor may get the impression that malleable castings are not very strong. This is not true. Malleable castings are not used in places where extremely heavy loads are handled, and it is very seldom that one of the heavier castings of this type finds its way to the welding shop.

Character of Malleable

In the case of small malleable iron castings, special attention should be given to the structure of the metal. The first part of the production process for a malleable casting is to make a plain iron casting which is known to be brittle and unworkable throughout. The casting is then annealed for a number of hours and cooled very slowly. This produces a section having two distinct structures, the inside being brittle cast iron and the outside being softer and more resistant to shock. A malleable casting is easily recognized when broken because these different zones are clearly defined.

There are two different occasions when repairs are made to malleable castings. The first case is in the foundry when difficulties are observed before the heat treatment has been given to the casting. In this case it is a simple cast iron welding operation. The second case is that of the malleable casting broken in service. This is entirely different. No satisfactory method of welding with any kind of iron or steel welding rod has been found. It might be possible to make such a repair if the whole casting could be heat treated after welding, but generally speaking it would be less expensive and more satisfactory to obtain a new casting. The influence of the heat and the actual welding operation will destroy some of the important properties of the malleable casting.

Bronze Welding

However, a repair can be made by using a bronze filler rod. A vee should be cut by any accepted means down to the bottom of the fracture. The pieces are set together very carefully and heated only enough to melt the bronze filler rod. If a good flux is used the bronze will penetrate all the way through the crack and make a good bond with both pieces. An excess of heat will not only be harmful to the malleable casting but will also cause a loss of the zinc in the bronze and thus weaken the resulting joint. Some operators prefer what is called a manganese bronze for this purpose because it melts at a lower temperature. Repairs in malleable castings have been made with a manganese bronze filler rod and microphotographs taken to show the amount of heat used was not enough to change the structure of the malleable casting. This is practical and an ideal result in making this type of repair.

Wrought Iron

Wrought iron is a highly refined iron of high purity, low in carbon in which is incorporated a minutely and uniformly distributed quantity of slag. One of its characteristics is its high resistance to corrosion. There is a definite grain to this metal which is in a way comparable to that of wood. On this account it has greater strength in the direction of the grain and approximately 25% less across the grain. Fabricators should always bear this point in mind when the material is being used.

Torch Technique

Due to the slag inclusion in the metal, the weldor when first working with wrought iron may be misled into thinking that the fusion point has been reached long before the metal is ready for adding material. The slag at about 2,100 F gives the metal a pasty appearance—far below the fusion point. A higher temperature of the order of 2,700-2,770 F is required and it is essential that the flame be kept constantly on a sizeable puddle of molten metal and maintained all the time material is being added. Care must also be exercised in seeing that the puddle completely penetrates the thickness of the material being welded.

If theory is followed, it would be logical to use a Swedish iron filler rod or other rod low in carbon if the characteristics of wrought iron are to be maintained. However, there are commercial low carbon steel rods on the market which produce satisfactory results so far as strength and corrosion resistance are concerned.

Chrome Moly Steel

This material is very popular in aircraft construction and the welding of chrome molybdenum steel tubing has become a fine art in many American airplane factories.

It is an extremely tough, strong material and can be welded with entire success, but the weldor must perfect his technique to obtain the best results. Preparation of the parts usually calls for square cut ends which must be cleaned inside and out well past the width to be welded with tack welds to set the pieces in position before making the regular welds.

Flame Adjustment

A light torch is needed that may be easily handled without fatigue and of such dimension that the weldor can easily reach all parts to be welded. Most manufacturers have developed a special torch for this type of work. The flame adjustment should be strictly neutral and provision made for exact regulation of the gases all during the welding operation. An oxidizing flame will burn the metal so that it will tend to crack on cooling. A carburizing flame, on the other hand, will add carbon to the deposit making it brittle. The tip used should be only large enough to handle the metal at hand. Too large a tip will overheat the metal, making for weakness in the weld.

Welding Technique

Experience has shown that it is not advisable to use a filler material of the same composition as the tubing. A popular type contains about 0.10% to 0.15% carbon and 0.10% to 0.30% manganese. Penetration all the way through the material is a standard requirement with reinforcement from $1/16$ to $1/8$ in. Where it is possible, better work can be done if the weld is made in a vertical position progressing from the bottom upward. When tack welds are reached care must be taken to see that they are completely melted and fused and not just skimmed over. Flux is not necessary, but the weld metal must be kept clean and free of oxides and slag inclusions. This is accomplished by continuing the weld from start to finish once it is begun keeping the puddle covered with the flame and its envelope.

Welding Precautions

While chrome molybdenum tubing is daily being welded with entire success, there are some precautions that the weldor must keep in mind if he is to be among those who are turning out acceptable work. This metal while tough and strong when cold is even weaker than mild steel at elevated temperatures therefore it must not be subjected to stresses and shocks while at a white heat. Welding should preferably be done in a location free from all drafts, for there will be a tendency for the metal to chill too fast and thus be weakened. Tightly clamped jigs should never be used. Rather the parts should be free to move as the weld and tubing cools, thus avoiding breaks. Starting at an edge is not to be recommended. Start at a point away from the edge and work to it, if necessary drawing the flame slightly away from the joint so as not to overheat it when the edge itself is reached. Do not knock finished parts out of the jig onto the floor while still at a white heat, for they will break.

High Carbon Steel

It is probably more difficult to give exact instructions for welding on high carbon steel than for any other metal. The reason for this is that after we depart from what is ordinarily termed mild steel having a very low carbon content we get into a series of steels showing a great many different percentages of carbon and many of these steels will also contain important percentages of other elements such as manganese, nickel, vanadium, etc. Steels with a higher carbon content are made for hard-

Spark Test Data

	Metal	Volume of Stream	Relative Length of Stream, Inches†
1.	Wrought iron	Large	65
2.	Machine steel	Large	70
3.	Carbon tool steel	Moderately large	55
4.	Gray cast iron	Small	25
5.	White cast iron	Very small	20
6.	Annealed mall. iron	Moderate	30
7.	High speed steel	Small	60
8.	Manganese steel	Moderately large	45
9.	Stainless steel	Moderate	50
10.	Tungsten-chromium die steel	Small	35
11.	Nitrided Nitralloy	Large (curved)	55
12.	Stellite	Very small	10
13.	Cemented tungsten carbide	Extremely small	2
14.	Nickel	Very small**	10
15.	Copper, brass, aluminum	None	

†Figures obtained with 12″ wheel on bench stand and are relative only. Actual length in each instance will vary with grinding wheel, pressure, etc.

ness, strength, toughness, or combinations of these qualities. Very often they are not only heat treated, but mechanically treated, i.e., forged or rolled.

OXY-ACETYLENE WELDOR'S HANDBOOK 151

from The Welding Encyclopedia, 17th Edition

[Spark test illustrations: 7. High Speed Steel, 8. Manganese Steel, 9. Stainless Steel, 10. Tungsten-Chrom. Die Steel, 11. Nitrided Nitralloy, 12. Stellite, 13. Cemented Tungsten Carbide, 14. Nickel]

Color of Stream Close to Wheel	Color of Streaks Near End of Stream	Quantity of Spurts	Nature of Spurts	
Straw	White	Very few	Forked	1.
White	White	Few	Forked	2.
White	White	Very many	Fine, repeating	3.
Red	Straw	Many	Fine, repeating	4.
Red	Straw	Few	Fine, repeating	5.
Red	Straw	Many	Fine, repeating	6.
Red	Straw	Extremely few	Forked	7.
White	White	Many	Fine, repeating	8.
Straw	White	Moderate	Forked	9.
Red	Straw*	Many	Fine, repeating	10.
White	White	Moderate	Forked	11.
Orange	Orange	None		12.
Light Orange	Light Orange	None		13.
Orange	Orange	None		14.
		None		15.

*Blue-white spurts. **Some wavy streaks.
(Reprinted from (Norton Co.) "Grits and Grinds" June 1940.)

Character of High Carbon

The weldor should bear in mind that he is not able to duplicate exactly the heat treatment or mechanical treatment given to the original piece. In general, high carbon steels are used for tools. They melt at a lower temperature than mild steel and show signs of sparkling when overheated. This last is a useful property to the weldor because excessive sparkling indicates that too much heat is being used in the weld. There is no objection to using a mild steel rod or its equivalent when welding broken tool steel pieces because although the filler rod is not as strong as the original piece, its ductility is a valuable quality and if attention is given to securing a good sound deposit a very serviceable and dependable weld can be expected.

Welding Procedure

The important feature to watch is the amount of heat used. This should be kept as low as possible and the weldor must learn to deposit this metal and get away with the least possible delay. It should also be noted that high carbon steel is quite frequently used as a filler rod for building up surfaces which are subjected to hard wear. Such a weld requires chilling to get the hardest surface.

The hardest of these steels are commonly called high speed steels, and such alloys are used for metal cutting tools. They are very expensive, so it is usually cheaper to make a complete tool by welding a tip of high speed onto a shank of lower carbon steel. This can be done with a nickel steel rod working backward from the cutting end to the body of the shank. The reason for this is that the low carbon steel of the shank will absorb heat more rapidly than the high carbon steel on the tip. As the flame is progressing toward the shank, the high carbon tip is therefore subjected to as little heat as possible and the shank will absorb most of it. It is not advisable to make up cutting tools in this way on large scale unless facilities are available for heat treating.

Heat treatment is necessary when maximum strength is called for and quick cooling or chilling is necessary when maximum hardness is desired.

Low Alloy Steels

Those metals which are now commercially referred to as "low alloy" are in no sense new to metal fabricators. They have recently found wider aplication on account of various characteristics desirable to fabricators. In the main their high strength, making for less weight in finished fabrications and corrosion resistance assuring long life have been responsible for current popularity and widespread use. Almost every producer makes a steel of this class and the analyses vary almost as widely as the number of mills rolling the product.

Despite the wide variance of the alloying constituents, in general they all follow the same characteristics of being relatively low in carbon. Those falling into the group having 0.15% or less carbon are readily weldable and no difficulty subsequent to welding is experienced. However, when the carbon ranges higher, approximately up to 0.30%, which makes up a second general group, air hardening in the weld area is encountered which must be taken into consideration during welding or subsequent to the welding operation. Still a third group, in which the carbon content generally ranges over 0.30%, must be given extra consideration from the point of view of welding. In general they all require stress relieving. Preheating of the metal prior to welding is also helpful.

Because of the great number of these metals on the market and the variations in the alloying constituents, it is next to impossible to suggest a general welding procedure. When encountered, the best recommendations that can be given, is to contact the manufacturer of the specific steel in question asking for a procedure control.

Manganese-Steel

Steel containing a relatively large amount of manganese is widely used for parts which are subject to great wear, such as railroad frogs and crossings, dipped teeth, etc. The fusion point of manganese steel is given as 2,400 F. This is a low melting point for steel and indicates that the weldor must be careful not to overheat the metal. The manganese content causes considerable difficulty in welding as the metal has a strong tendency to foam.

Welding Procedure

A good many weldors do not try to build up a worn manganese piece with the manganese filler rod but use a high carbon rod or a hard surface metal instead. If it is desired to build them up with a manganese rod, good quality rod should be obtained. The weld should be started with the parent metal cool and if possible it should be kept immersed in water in order to keep cool. This can sometimes be done by building a basin of clay around the part to be welded and filling it with water. A slight excess of acetylene in the flame will be helpful. More metal should be added a little at a time and chilled with cold water as it is added. The work will be improved by vigorous annealing. Better results can sometimes be obtained on the smaller manganese castings because on account of their small size they can be preheated and the welding can be done with a large pool. The only precaution necessary is to avoid rubbing with the filler rod. After welding the whole piece should be reheated to a uniform temperature of 1900 F for 30 minutes and then quenched in warm water by complete submersion.

Stainless-Steel

Nickel and chromium when combined with steel produce an alloy popularly known as stainless steel. Wide use is made of the material both because of its corrosion resisting properties and its high strength. There are various analyses, the more common of which is known as 18-8. By this is meant that there is approximately 18% chromium and 8% nickel. The percentages vary with different manufacturers, but the general characteristics are the same. Another analysis in general use is known as 25-12. In addition to chromium and nickel another important element having a bearing on weldability is carbon. Where it is held to 0.07% or under there is no difficulty in welding. However, when the amount of carbon ranges higher, carbide precipitation develops within the welding range and heat treating facilities should be available. However, this objectionable feature can be overcome by using parent metal to which has been added a slight amount of columbium and making the weld with a filler rod of the same material.

Preparing Stainless

Parts to be welded should be carefully cleaned by any accepted method. If the work being done is on sheets, they should be tack welded or positioned in a jig so that warping will not occur. This step is essential, for stainless steel will not conduct heat rapidly and expands more quickly than ordinary steel when heat is applied. The jig, particularly if it is possible to place a heavy piece of metal close to the joint, will absorb the heat from the metal being welded and thus prevent warpage. A good flux is essential and should be prepared especially for stainless welding. Apply it to the bottom of the weld and also to the welding rod itself.

Welding Technique

The tip selected should be one or two sizes smaller than required for steel of comparable thickness. Extreme care must be exercised to maintain a strictly neutral flame or slight excess of acetylene which should be no longer than the inner cone. The weld should be carried along as fast as possible, using the forward method so that the welding rod will melt at approximately the same time the parent metal reaches that temperature. If facilities are available, it is helpful to the characteristics of the weld to cool the deposited metal with an air blast. With the weld completed the deposited metal should be ground flush and preferably polished. This operation will remove all oxides and restore the stainless characteristics at the weld zone. The use of iron files or chipping hammers is discouraged for such practice has been known to start rusting.

Selecting the Rod

The welding rod if it contains the proper amount of either columbium or molybdenum will produce better results than one having these elements omitted. With rods of this type a mildly carburizing flame is permissible and might be recommended where difficulty is experienced in maintaining a neutral adjustment. It should be held at the tip of the cone of the flame and the envelope should cover the puddle and the material ahead. Puddling is to be avoided. Rather keep the molten metal as quiet as possible. Silver brazing can also be used as a means of making strong, corrosion resisting joints. It should be kept in mind if this method is used, that all joints should be overlapped the required amount to develop the necessary strength.

Stainless Clad Steels

Stainless clad steels are furnished with a corrosion resisting material on one face of the sheet or plate. They are finding wider use because of their economy. The clad section varies in analysis with the mill rolling the material. In general these metals lend themselves readily to welded fabrication if the correct procedure is followed.

Usually joint preparation follows recommendations for comparable thickness of steel with the exception that a vee, if required, is cut from the steel side, only the thickness of the steel. On the clad side the same is true, the vee is only cut to the depth of the cladding. Preparation for welding as regards fluxing, type of flame and torch manipulation and selection of welding rod follow the recommendations for the individual metals being welded. It is usual practice to weld the steel side first. One precaution that must be observed is to chip out the bottom of the vee from the clad side completely removing any metal that has worked through from the steel welding operation. It is recommended that a cut with a round nosed chisel extend well into the steel weld beyond the depth of the cladding.

Chromium Alloys

Within recent years numerous alloys containing varying percentages of chromium have been made available. Their merit of resisting corrosion has gained them ready acceptance with both fabricators and users whose equipment must withstand severe service. In general, the several groups contain the element chromium within the following ranges: 3.0 - 6.0% Cr.; 12.0 - 14.0% Cr.; and 15.0 - 18.0% Cr. Other analyses are available but those mentioned are in most frequent use. The carbon content of the three groups never exceed 0.12%.

Preparation of the metals to be welded is simple and follows generally the steps required in plain carbon steels.

Preparing and Fluxing

For example, light sheets should be flanged with the flange not exceeding $1/8$ in.; up to $1/8$ in. sheets may be butted producing satisfactory results, while thicknesses above ⅛ in. should be beveled. A special flux capable of dissolving oxides and which is made especially for welding metals of this type should be applied both to the top and bottom of the seam and, in addition, to the welding rod. This for the reason that chromium oxides are highly infusible and when they appear on the surface of the weld puddle make it difficult to penetrate with the heat to the bottom of the weld.

Torch Technique

Chromium readily combines with both oxygen and carbon at raised temperatures; so it is extremely important that the welding flame be carefully adjusted. If too much oxygen is used oxides are formed producing porous, brittle welds. Excess carbon (carburizing flame), on the other hand, develops chromium carbides which are detrimental to a good weld. Further, loss of chromium in the weld reduces the corrosion resistant qualities of the metal. Any deviation of flame adjustment should be only mildly on the carburizing side. It is well to use a welding rod which is columbium bearing, for it produces a good deposit and, on account of the affinity of columbium for carbon, the possibility of formation of chromium carbides is practically eliminated. The tip used must be the smallest practicable and the molten puddle kept as small as possible. The greatest speed consistent with the thickness of the metal should be used to prevent overheating, for boiling, which will result, produces a porous, weak weld.

At times various applications of an 18-8 filler material have been made where the parts being welded could not be annealed, were not to be subjected to severe corrosive conditions, or where the highest physical properties of the metal were not required. However the practice is not recommended where high strength or resistance to corrosion are requirements unless subsequent annealing can be resorted to. Even under the circumstances the highest physical properties nor the best corrosion resisting characteristics can not be obtained.

Where there is some possible latitude in the preparation of the joint and corrosion problems can be met, silver brazing can be used with entire success in joining these metals. The high temperature necessary to make a fusion weld is not needed and if a lap seam is permissible, adequate strength can be developed.

If the metals require heat-treatment or annealing after welding, it is only to be recommended that this type of work be done in shops where necessary facilities are available in the hands of experienced men. At times it is possible to anneal the weld with the torch flame by bringing it up to a red heat for from one to three minutes, thus reducing the brittle zone in and adjacent to the weld.

Welding Copper

Copper is a red metal having a specific gravity of 8.9, a melting point of 1,981 F and a tensile strength of 25,000 psi in castings, and 60,000 psi when cold worked. The chances for complete success in the welding of copper depend a good deal upon whether the welding is for repair or in production. This is because there are two kinds of copper used commercially. One of these is electrolytic copper, which contains a small amount of oxygen in the form of cuprous oxide. Another kind of copper is called deoxidized copper, which is quite easy to weld. When it is a question of repair work the weldor is obliged to do the best he can on the metal which is brought to him, and if it is not deoxidized copper, should not expect too much in the way of results. However, if it is a question of making a copper tank, the weldor can make sure of success by seeing that deoxidized copper is used for the tank material.

Electrolytic Copper

A brief explanation of differences between these types of copper may be helpful. Copper as brought to the refinery is in the form of rough slabs which contain metallic impurities. These are separated by an electro-plating process and the nearly pure metal secured in this manner is melted in the furnace and then cast into slabs and bars. When melted in the furnace some of the copper is oxidized and the oxide is dissolved in the molten metal. Some of this oxide is removed before pouring, but there is always a small amount of it left and this oxide gives trouble when the copper is welded, for it melts sooner than the pure copper and spreads out along the grain boundaries where a small amount of oxide seriously weakens the structure.

It is apparent that regardless of how well actual welding is performed and how sound the metal is which is deposited, the presence of the oxides near the weld will cause a weak zone. It has also been found that if the weld is made in a reducing atmosphere, that is, with a reducing flame, the oxide near the joint develops a spongy structure. There is some free hydrogen present in the reducing atmosphere and this finds its way through a few thousandths of an inch into the red hot copper uniting with the cuprous oxide to produce the spongy copper and also water vapor. The latter develops a pressure which has a tendency to break up the copper and leaves a weak zone after the copper has solidified. One authority places the tensile strength limit of 15,000 to 18,000 pounds per square inch on welds in electrolytic copper when made with copper filler rod. Stronger joints than this, however, can be made by using brazing brass or silver brazing alloy inasmuch as these metals will make a strong bond in copper at temperatures below the melting point of the oxide. Therefore, brazing and silver brazing are to be recommended for the repair of electrolytic copper when maximum strength is desired.

Deoxidized Copper

Deoxidized copper is easily welded with the oxyacetylene torch and should be welded with deoxidized copper rod. It is easily obtained commercially and should be specified whenever the material is to be used for welding, to make tanks or other copper articles. A deoxidized copper containing a small amount of silicon is usually recommended. This metal will be much easier to weld than the electrolytic copper and the structure will have practically twice as much strength. The use of the deoxidized copper welding rod when welding electrolytic copper will give a strong weld, but still does not prevent the formation of the weak zone in the immediate vicinity of the weld.

Welding Technique

Copper should be welded with a neutral flame and a welding rod free from manganese should always be used. It will be noticed at once that the metal conducts heat so fast that the surrounding metal will become red hot at a greater distance, before a weld can be made, than in the case of welding steel and iron. The repair welding procedures described for the welding of steel will give the most satisfactory results as a rule. In the case of very thick materials, some expense can be saved by preheating ahead of the weld with some sort of preheating torch. In fact, this procedure is to be recommended for thicknesses which would be considered light material in steel or iron. A considerable waste is involved in using the torch flame to produce sufficient heat for the formation of a good welding puddle.

Control of Molten Metal

One of the most common defects found in copper welds is failure to get the adjacent metal hot enough, with the result that heat is conducted away from the welding zone, the faces of the bevel becoming cool while the puddle is being formed. The puddle therefore, has a chance to run over onto metal which is not liquid enough to fuse with it, and simply sticks there lightly, although the weldor gets the impression that he is securing a good solid weld. The way to prevent this defect is not to attempt to get sufficient heat by using an extra large flame, but to take the time and patience to have the adjacent metal thoroughly preheated and then weld it with a flame of the correct size. It is also inadvisable to try to force the fusion by bringing the white cone of the neutral flame too close to the metal.

Precautions and Hints

A practical and important precaution to take in the welding of copper and all copper alloys is to avoid going over the weld at any point without adding additional filler metal. There is often a temptation to remelt the deposited metal in order to improve its appearance, but this should not be done unless it is practicable to add filler rod at the same time.

There are some cases when the line of weld is accessible to both sides and when this is true a substitute for preheating can be found in using another torch on the reverse side of the weld. This does not work very well on long seams because of the difficulty in making uniform progress with both torches, and therefore, in case of long seams preheating may be better done by keeping a slow fire underneath the work.

When welding on copper which is not very thick, some weldors find it helpful to keep a sheet of asbestos paper underneath the weld. If the work is flat the asbestos paper can be supported on a sheet of some other material and if it is round the asbestos can be wrapped around a piece of pipe of suitable diameter. This device often serves the purpose of preventing the original material from sinking in the vicinity of the weld.

As far as the manipulation of the torch is concerned, it is important to keep the white cone about $\frac{1}{4}$ in. away from the molten metal and not expose the metal too long to the intense heat. Prefluxing the welding rod will eliminate frequent removal from the puddle. The entire flame should be directed on the weld metal already deposited and the adjacent base metal keeping both molten while additional metal is being added. The melting of the bottom of the weld and all beveled faces should be progressive and always accompanied by the melting of the welding rod.

Welding Brass

Different alloys of copper which are classified as brasses are so numerous that any attempt to list them would serve only to confuse the weldor. The principal ingredients of brass are either copper and zinc or copper, tin and zinc. The different brasses in common use vary greatly in color, composition and physical properties. Most of them, however, are easy to weld by the oxy-acetylene process, particularly if a good welding flux is used.

Filler Rod Selection

It is often possible to make a splendid weld by using a filler rod of the same material as the parts being welded. Sometimes, however, it is desirable to select a brass filler material which has a lower melting point than the brass being welded, so that the latter does not have to be completely melted. Very often this procedure results in the strongest possible weld. One reason for this is probably that the lower temperature used makes it possible to secure a joint with very little change in the grain structure of the metal. There is also some economy of time and materials involved, because when metal of lower melting point is used for filler material, it is not necessary to use the amount of preheating which is required when the filler material is of the same composition as the parent metal.

Flame Adjustment

If a strictly neutral flame is used to melt the parent metal, it will be found that zinc will begin to come off in heavy white fumes. This is not a proper condition, for the relation of the elements in the metal will be disturbed. However, if the flame is slowly adjusted to oxidizing, it will be noticed that the fuming will stop and that a coating will develop on the surface of the metal. If further oxygen is added to the flame this coating will become increasingly heavy to the point where it will be difficult to proceed with the weld. Judgment in the degree of the oxidizing flame adjustment is required. Recommendation is that further oxygen be turned on after the first definite evidence of the film is seen. In the hands of an experienced operator the strictly neutral flame can be used satisfactorily if it is held back a slight distance from the molten metal, at which point it has slightly oxidizing characteristics.

The theory of this flame adjustment is that the use of an excess of oxygen causes the formation on the surface of the puddle of a pasty film which contains a certain proportion of oxide of zinc and that this film prevents the boiling away of the zinc in the welding puddle. An additional recommendation is that the flux should be applied to the reverse side of the weld where it can act on the metal which is not reached by the flame itself.

The size of the torch tip to use should be greater than that which would be necessary for the same thickness of mild steel. Care should be exercised to clean the metal adjacent to the weld very thoroughly and be prepared to work fast because brass is very fluid when it is melted and if an excessive amount of heating is done blow holes are quite apt to be formed. Select a good flux and see that plenty of it is used. Never do any remelting of brass welds without adding new metal. If the weld metal does not seem to have good clean structure and is somewhat porous, it may be improved by light hammering.

Welding Bronze

Bronze is one of the well known alloys of copper. A great many articles are made of it, and there is quite a long list of alloys of copper and tin which come under the general classification of bronze. Tin is not a very strong metal, having a tensile strength from 4,000 to 5,000 psi and a very low melting point; that is, around 450 F. Although it is very soft, it has a great hardening property when added to copper so that some of the bronzes made by alloying copper with tin develop tensile strengths up to 50,000 psi. It is likewise true that these alloys are easy to weld, because, although the tin melts at a low temperature it does not boil away easily and the result is that the alloy melts and flows smoothly without losing any of its important properties.

Flux Is Needed

The fact that bronze flows so readily has sometimes led weldors to consider that it can be welded without the use of any flux. It is doubtful, however, that such welds can be made consistently without formation of oxides.

Therefore, it is advisable to use a good grade of brazing flux whenever bronze is being welded. Good fluxes are made of fused borax, borax mixed with boric acid, or sodium carbonate.

Know the Analysis

The wide range of different compositions which are classified as bronze makes it necessary for the weldor to know something of the composition of the bronze on which he is working in order to get the best results. The difference in the temperatures at which the different constituents become solid may easily result in their being solidified at different times which would naturally set up zones of weakness. Therefore, if the bronze contains a large percentage of tin, the pool should be kept as small as possible and the metal should be cooled quickly after the weld is made. This applies to bronze containing 10% or more tin. Bronze containing only 5% tin is not apt to suffer from slower cooling.

The precaution noted regarding copper welding to the effect that the metal should not be welded without adding metal from the filler rod at the same time should be repeated here in case of bronze welding.

Good results in bronze welding demand that the metal should not be reheated after welding to give the weld a good appearance, as this sets up expansion stresses which lead to cracking through the weld.

Preparation of Joint

Good results in bronze welding demand that the work be carefully beveled and thoroughly clean before the weld starts. If they are preheated, care should be taken to see that no strain is put upon them or that they are not severely jarred when they are heated to a temperature near the fusion point. Keep the white cone of the welding flame a slight distance away from the metal and avoid holding the flame too long in one position as this has a tendency to cause a segregation of the tin in the alloy. After the flux has been applied, manipulate the filler rod and torch so that the filler rod and the work are melted at about the same time. Preheating is of considerable value because it makes it possible to advance the weld rapidly, which is a great advantage in welding bronze.

The bronze welding rod is used to considerable extent in making repairs on metals other than bronze. This subject is discussed in detail in another chapter of this book.

Welding Nickel

Nickel is a metal which is found mostly in chemical equipment or equipment which is subjected to contact with corrosive materials. It has a melting point of 2,645 F, and is known to be especially sensitive to the conditions under which it is melted. The welding methods advocated for nickel are intended to avoid the absorption of sulphur, carbon, oxygen and other gases. In general, a high heat in the weld is desirable in order to secure localization of the fusing action. Considerable skill is necessary to use this highly localized heat without losing some of the essential elements of the parent metal and also causing the absorption of undesirable ones.

Torch Technique

The difficulty of welding nickel is somewhat reduced if the tip is inclined so as to throw the flame, which should be neutral or only slighting carburizing, backward away from the direction of the weld rather than forward on the unwelded material. Using the reverse direction of the flame delays the solidification of the deposited nickel and this has a beneficial effect. The operator will notice when he starts welding that a scum will form on the surface of the molten metal. When this scum becomes so thick that it makes the welding difficult, it is best not to try to use a flux to remove it. If a flux is used there is more danger of its acting too strongly and really spoiling the weld from the point of view of soundness.

Adding the Welding Rod

The welding rod used should be commercially pure nickel, bright-annealed and free from oxides. The rod should be held in the envelope flame until near the melting temperature before being introduced into the molten puddle. When it has reached the proper temperature and the metal is being added to the weld, the rod should be left there with a minimum of puddling and disturbance of the molten metal. The flame should be kept playing over the weld at all times to protect it from the atmosphere. Shocks or hammering of the weld metal while hot should be avoided since it is extremely brittle because of its hot short characteristics.

Use of Jigs

Jigs for the welding of sheets are a distinct benefit in controlling expansion and contraction of the metal. If the work being done is on a production basis, it will save time if a fixture is developed which can be easily loaded and the finished work removed. A practical device can be assembled from angle iron and C-clamps where the volume of work does not warrant a more expensive set-up. A back-up or chill bar slightly grooved just beneath the weld area should be incorporated in any such device used.

Where a product is to be fabricated from sheets or thin plates of nickel and the design is flexible enough so that lapping of edges is not objectionable, silver brazing offers a method of making a strong, sound joint. This process, using a heat well under the zone at which nickel is hot-short eliminates the need for skill in torch welding.

An important physical property of nickel which may seriously affect the welding is that its strength is very low at the temperature just below the melting point. Therefore, if a welded seam is remelted this should never start at an exposed edge but a couple of inches of cool metal should be left to take up the stresses caused by the heat. Starting to reweld at an exposed edge usually has the effect of starting a crack which will follow the entire course of the torch.

Monel Metal

Monel metal is an alloy of nickel and copper, produced in the form of rods, sheets, castings, and other standard shapes. The melting point is 2,480 F with heat conductivity of about $1/15$ that of copper. This metal is used widely in the chemical industries on account of its great resistance to the action of various chemicals. There is seldom any necessity for repair welding on monel metal, but welding is often used in the construction of articles made of this alloy, particularly tanks, pipes and fittings.

Torch Adjustment

Due to the fact that an oxidizing flame is always harmful when welding copper or any alloy or copper, except some of the brasses, a neutral flame is recommended for welding monel metal. If in doubt regarding the flame regulation, it is possible to use a flame which is only slightly carburizing, but addition of carbon in the weld is not desirable. In general, the welding tip used should be one or two sizes larger than the tip which would be used for the same thickness of steel.

Flux and Filler Rod

Flux should not be used unless the metal has an excessive amount of oxide on the surface. In this case borax brazing flux will be helpful. As a rule the thin film of oxide which forms on the surface of the puddle when welding monel metal is really helpful and should not be destroyed by flux. Use bright monel metal wire for filler rod and when preparing the work see to it that there is no possibility of a draft striking the weld, as this will

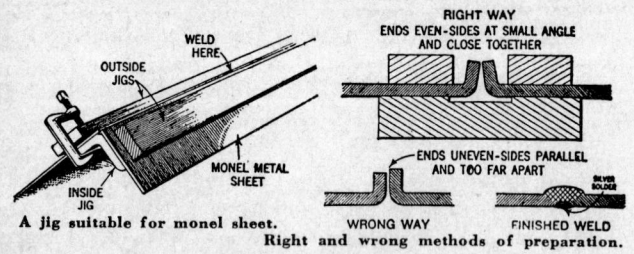

A jig suitable for monel sheet.

Right and wrong methods of preparation.

make it brittle. Plan to complete the welding in one place before starting in another and make the whole weld in a long seam at one pass rather than in layers. Also build up the weld considerably above the surface. If any impurities or foreign matter are noticed in the puddle these should be floated to the top by melting underneath them so that the slag can be ground off when the weld is finished.

Welding Technique

Use clean welding rod and have the edges of the weld thoroughly clean and bright before applying the flame. Use a 90 deg. bevel on anything thicker than 1/8 in. It is a good plan to have the edges of the weld heated to a dull red a short distance ahead before starting to form the puddle. Be careful to see that the sides and bottom of the bevel are well fused and that the welding rod is heated practically to the melting point before putting it into the puddle. Do not work the welding rod in the puddle but hold it quietly underneath the surface. Avoid holding the flame for a long time on one spot. If the piece being welded is so thick that it has been beveled from both sides, preheat the line of weld after welding from one side before starting a second weld. Allow the weld to cool slowly when it is finished and if maximum strength is desired, hammer it while it is still hot.

When welding monel metal sheets it is advisable to use well constructed jigs, preferably with a chill bar beneath the weld. Take care that the jigs do not clamp the metal too tightly, and space the sheet $3/16$ to $1/4$ in. per ft. of weld. Weld the thin sheets as rapidly as possible, using a flux is necessary to get maximum speed.

Monel Castings

The welding of monel castings is required occasionally and the weldor will find it helpful to be guided by his experience in welding cast iron. No flux need be used. The important part of the procedure is proper preheating. The best form of preheating is usually to preheat the entire casting in a furnace and to keep it well covered with asbestos paper while welding, then allow it to cool as slowly and evenly as possible.

Sometimes on account of the complicated nature of the casting and the location of breaks it is difficult to determine how to preheat the job so as to prevent cooling cracks. In such cases it might be advisable to repair it with brazing spelter or silver brazing alloy, either of which can be used without raising the casting to a high enough temperature to cause cracking.

Lead Welding

Years ago the operation of welding lead was given the name of "lead burning" by manufacturers and repairers of storage batteries. The term is very inaccurate because lead is not burned if the welding is properly done. Lead has a very low melting point (640 F) and is very fluid when melted. There are many weldors who consider the oxy-acetylene flame too hot for this metal and use some other fuel gas such as hydrogen, in place of acetylene.

Heat Control

However, it is not a very difficult matter to learn to control heat with the oxy-acetylene flame so as to make a good weld in this metal. It is seldom that any very thick sections will be encountered and for this reason operators sometimes conclude that beveling is not necessary. Quite on the contrary, it is best to bevel the edges almost to a knife edge on everything except the very thinnest sheet. It is very had to drive heat down through a pool of melted lead, so the only way to get full penetration is to bevel to the bottom so the welding can start from the bottom.

Controlling the Weld

The edges to be welded are first melted, then the heat is checked by putting strip of filler material in the flame and melting it into the bevel. Care must be taken to keep the edges melted in advance of the pool without overheating, so that the added metal will flow into the pool readily. It will be necessary to check the melting regularly by turning the flame aside for an instant. The best results therefore, are obtained by welding in a series of overlapping puddles instead of trying to run a ripple weld.

When the work is in a horizontal position a very neat job can be secured by making the weld in two or three layers. In this case the first layer is made without the addition of filler metal and simply weaving the flame back and forth over the seam to get a good union at the bottom. Succeeding layers are then welded with the use of adding material. Great care must be taken in these successive layers to make sure that the new metal is thoroughly fused with the metal beneath. The mistake most apt to be made by the inexperienced operator is to simply lay the new metal on the top of the previous layer without getting thorough fusion. If the weld has to be made in a vertical direction, or if it is in a rather thick section which requires a fairly definite contour, the weldor will save a good deal of time by using a mold to produce the desired shape.

Aluminum Welding

Aluminum is a metal very commonly used in industry. It is a very light metal and in the pure state it does not have a very high tensile strength. Except in the form of castings it can be worked and bent readily. The melting point is low, about 1218 F. One important property from the weldor's point of view that it oxidizes readily. A good indication of this is the fact that a piece of polished aluminum very soon becomes discolored when exposed to the air. The weldor should also note that quite a number of aluminum alloys are used which resemble pure aluminum in appearance. These alloys have other metals mixed with the aluminum so that the alloys themselves are very much stronger than pure aluminum. For the purpose of comparison it might be stated that the melting point is about one-half of that of cast iron and that aluminum conducts heat about three times as fast as cast iron. Aluminum will shrink more on cooling than cast iron and will also require less time for cooling because of the high thermal conductivity of aluminum.

The weldor should also note that when aluminum has been heated nearly to the melting point, it becomes very weak and in fact may fall apart of its own weight if not supported. It is not uncommon for a beginner on aluminum to find his gap getting larger instead of smaller as he continues to try to weld.

Aluminum is sometimes considered difficult to weld, but the experienced weldor who follows correct practice does not have any difficulty in producing a sound, strong weld in aluminum in any shape. It is successfully welded according to the standard joint designs. On account of its low melting point the work is reasonably fast and if care is taken to prevent the inclusion of oxides in the weld it is not difficult to secure a weld which can be finished so as to leave no trace of the location of the joint. The castings, of course, are somewhat brittle and there is danger of cracking if the proper preheating methods are not followed. The sheets are not so brittle but still require clever manipulation of the flame to get a first class job.

Gas welding of aluminum is generally confined to materials $1/32$ in. thick or over. For thinner materials, resistance welding is employed. Gas welding may be used to weld aluminum alloys in their various forms such as sheets, plates, etc. Alloys suited for general gas welding purposes are 2S, 3S, 52S and 61S.

Edge Preparation

The thickness of the material will largely determine the method of edge preparation. Generally, the edges are prepared in the same manner as the edges of similar thicknesses of steel. However, there are several noteworthy differences.

On thin material up to about 0.0625 in., no particular edge preparation is needed. Thin material of this type can usually be welded with a plain butt-type of weld.

The only requirement for the joint design is that the edges be straight and square.

If desired, these thin sheets (including those up to about 1/8 in.) may be welded with a flange-type of joint, Fig. 1. In this instance, the edge of each sheet is bent to form a flange having about the same height as the sheet is thick. The flange is melted down in the welding opera-

Fig. 1—(left) Thin sheets may be welded with a flange-type joint.
Fig. 2—(center) Unbeveled sheets up to 1/4 in. thick should be notched.
Fig. 3—(right) Plates over 1/4 in. thick should be beveled and notched.

tion and provides sufficient filler metal to render unnecessary the use of a filler rod in these thin gauge welding operations.

Unbeveled butt welds may be made on sheets up to 1/4 in. thick, but in these applications it is necessary to notch the sheets with a saw or a cold chisel in a manner similar to that shown in Fig. 2. Edge notching is recommended in aluminum welding because it serves to facilitate full weld penetration and also prevents local distortion and minimizes the likelihood of burning holes through the joint. Another important service of the notches is to provide channels down which flux may flow to the bottom of the weld. All butt welds in material over 1/8 in. thick are generally notched in some manner.

In the gas welding of plates over 1/4 in. thick, it

is highly desirable to bevel the edge to secure thorough penetration. The included angle of bevel may be 90 to 120 degrees. Single vee welds may be used on material up to about 7/16 in. thick, while a double vee butt weld is recommended for material over 7/16 in. In either event, notching is also recommended to supplement the beveled edges. If the plate is not notched, its reverse side should be chipped before welding.

Cleaning and Preheating

After the edges of the pieces have been properly prepared, the surface to be welded should be cleansed of grease, oil, dirt, etc. If the edges are heavily oxidized, it may be necessary to pickle them with acid, but as a general rule wire brushing with hot water is sufficient for oxide removal. The presence of grease and oil, however, may necessitate the use of gasoline, naphtha, carbon-tetrachloride or similar solvent to complete the cleaning job.

It is desirable to preheat when welding aluminum plates 1/4 in. thick or over in order to prevent cracks, assure more complete penetration and reduce gas consumption. Preheating to a temperature of 500 to 700 F is sufficient. Thin sheet aluminum should be warmed with the welding torch prior to welding; even this slight preheat helps to prevent cracks.

It is important that the preheating temperature does not exceed 700 F inasmuch as the desirable properties of certain aluminum alloys may be destroyed at higher temperatures. In preheating, if a pyrometer is not available, a mark made with carpenter's blue chalk will turn white at the proper preheating temperature for aluminum welding. Or if the part to be welded is rubbed with a pine stick, the mark will char at the proper preheating temperature. Again, cold aluminum gives a metallic ring when struck; this sound becomes duller as the temperature rises and disappears entirely at the temperature required for welding.

In preparing aluminum for gas welding it will be found highly desirable to jig the material wherever possible. Proper jigging gives adequate support to the parts being welded and thus helps greatly to avoid distortion, buckling and collapse of the items to be joined at high temperature.

The Welding Flame

A weldor undertaking the gas welding of aluminum will find that considerable care must be exercised to ascertain that a neutral flame is employed. In welding aluminum, a neutral or slightly reducing flame gives the best speed and economy as well as a clean weld of good soundness. Should the flame become oxidizing, it will cause the formation of aluminum oxide, resulting immediately in poor penetration and a defective weld.

Best results will be obtained in the gas welding of aluminum alloys when the proper size welding tip is used. Of course, it must be realized that the selection of the proper tip for use in welding aluminum alloys is largely a matter of experience, due allowance being made to take into consideration the skill of the weldor, the configuration of the weldment and various other uncontrolled factors. The more experienced weldor will be able to use the larger size tips and thereby increase his welding speed.

Welding Rods

The type of welding rod to be used will vary in accordance with the particular aluminum alloy that is to be welded. For welding 2S or 3S, a pure drawn aluminum wire (2S) is generally recommended, though for some lap joints a 5% silicon welding rod will produce slightly better results. This is also true for the welding of aluminum castings of 43 or 214.

The 5% silicon aluminum welding wire is likewise recommended for the other alloys, that is 52S, 53S and 61S, inasmuch as this rod possesses higher strength and good corrosion-resistant properties. The 5% silicon rod has a low melting point, which covers a wide melting range and consequently, remains plastic after the base metal has cooled. This characteristic makes it possible to shift any stresses set up by contraction—stresses which might cause cracking of the base metal on cooling — to the still plastic weld deposit.

Aluminum Fluxes

The use of the proper fluxes in the welding of aluminum is extremely important. Aluminum welding flux is designed to remove the aluminum oxide by chemically combining with it. The oxide forms rapidly in the molten weld pool, and unless it is removed a defective weld is sure to result. To insure the proper distribution of flux, it should be painted on the surface to be welded and also applied to the welding rod.

Aluminum flux is generally obtained in the powder form. It is best prepared by mixing the powder with water to form a thin, freely flowing paste. In this form, the flux may be brushed on the rod, or the rod may be dipped into it as welding proceeds. Care should be taken to avoid mixing more than a day's supply of flux paste inasmuch as it soon loses its efficacy. Also, the prepared flux should not be kept in steel containers as steel tends to contaminate the mixture.

It will be found advantageous to apply flux to the

prepared edges of the sheet or plate so as to prevent additional oxidation of these surfaces during the preheating and welding operations. It is particularly essential that adequate flux be applied to the edges of flanged joints since no filler rod is used in this welding operation. In all cases, the flux should be applied to both the top and bottom sides of the sheet in the area of the weld.

Care should be taken to remove all traces of adhering flux upon completion of the welding operation. It is recommended that the parts be washed in boiling water whenever possible; however, a steam jet may be used for cleaning them where steam is available. Flux may be removed rather easily by dropping the parts into cold water immediately after welding. This sudden quenching would have drastic effects on ferrous metals, but it does not appear to produce any undesirable results on aluminum. The parts may also be cleaned by immersing them for about 30 minutes in a hot 2% nitric acid solution or cold 10% sulphuric acid solution. Immersion in one of these solutions follows a soaking of about 3 minutes in hot water during which the weld joint is thoroughly scrubbed.

If so desired, butt welds in 2S and 3S may be peened at room or elevated temperatures. Peening produces a smooth surface finish, refines the grain structure, improves corrosion resistance, eliminates porosity, raises strength and reduces internal stresses.

Welding Technique

After the pieces to be welded have been properly prepared and fluxed, the flame is passed in ever smaller circles over the starting point until the flux melts or the rod begins to adhere to the surface. One of the major difficulties experienced by beginners in aluminum welding is the failure of the deposited metal to adhere.

This is generally caused by attempts to deposit the weld metal on cold base metal. After the flux melts, the base metal must be melted before the rod is applied, or else the base metal and the filler metal may be brought to the molten state simultaneously. To prevent oxidation, it is quite essential to keep the welding rod in the weld puddle all the time—somewhat difficult to do on thin sheets.

Forehand welding is generally considered best for the welding of aluminum since the flame points away from the completed weld and thus preheats the edges to be welded. Too rapid melting is also prevented. The torch should be held at a low angle (less than 30 deg. above horizontal) when welding thin sheets. For thicker sheets ($3/16$ in. and above), the angle of the torch should be increased to nearer the vertical. Changing of the angle of the torch to accord with the thickness minimizes the likelihood of burning through the sheet during welding.

When welding sheet aluminum, there is little need to impart any motion to the torch other than moving it forward. On flanged sheets, care should be taken to break the oxide film as the flange melts down. This task may be accomplished by stirring the melted flange with a rod.

With aluminum plate (above $3/16$ in.), the torch should be given a uniform (but not unduly) lateral motion in order to distribute the weld metal over the entire width of the weld. A slight back and forth motion will assist the flux in its removal of oxides. The rod should be dipped into the weld puddle periodically and withdrawn from the puddle with a forward motion. This method of withdrawal closes the puddle, prevents porosity and assists the flux to remove the oxide film.

Aluminum welds should be made in a single pass so far as possible. This is especially true of alloys having a poor fluidity.

It must be remembered that the angle of the torch has much to do with welding speed. Instead of lifting the flame from time to time in order to avoid melting holes in the sheet, it will be found advantageous to hold the welding torch at a flatter angle, thus increasing the speed. The speed of welding should also be increased as the edge of the sheet is approached.

While the previous discussion concerns welding in the flat position, it might be well to add that aluminum can also be welded in the vertical position. In this instance, the torch is given an up and down rather than a rotating motion. On the thicker materials, it will be found advantageous to use two torches, one on each side of the joint, so that the weld may be completed on both sides at the same time. The rod is stirred in the weld puddle as in the case of flat welding.

Aluminum, it should be noted, cannot be welded overhead.

Heat-Treatable Alloys

Most aluminum fabrications, particularly in the making of metal furniture and architectural products, call for materials of high strength. As a rule, 53S or 61S alloys are used for such applications. These materials can be welded quite readily by the oxy-acetylene welding technique, in general quite similar to that used for the non-heat-treatable alloys. The greater likelihood for contraction strains (leading ultimately to cracking) necessitates a slight change in the general welding procedure.

Heat-treatable alloys should be jigged for welding. The clamps of the jig should be placed as far as possible from the joint so that there will be less stress in the weld and hence less danger of cracking. The likelihood of cracking can be eliminated greatly by the use of a 5% silicon aluminum welding rod. Having a lower melting point than the aluminum alloys, this rod permits the base metal to solidify before the weld pool freezes. As the weld is the last area to solidify, all of the contraction strains will be in the weld bead rather than throughout the base metal.

In the welding of heat-treatable alloys, it will be found that cracking may be lessened by tack welding the parts while they are in the jig and then loosening the clamps before completing the seam.

In welding heat-treatable alloys, the weld should be made in one pass. Single pass welding, incidentally, is usually cheaper and more economical than multiple pass welding.

Extreme care must be exercised in peening welds on 53S or 61S alloys because of the tendency towards cracking during this operation. Should a flush bead be desired, it may be obtained by chipping the weld bead as closely as possible and then peening lightly for the finishing operation. Welds on heat-treatable alloys may be finished very satisfactorily by grinding or buffing.

53S and 61S have satisfactory metallurgical characteristics imparted to them by solution heat treatment. Welding naturally destroys some of the effects of this heat treatment by lowering the strength of the parent metal in the weld zone. Hence, it is not generally possible to predict the strength of such materials following welding. If it is necessary to know the strength of a particular piece accurately, it is recommended that individual welds be tested.

Naturally, base annealed 53S or 61S alloys can

be welded without effect upon the mechanical properties. In fact, it is not at all unusual to find that the weld is stronger than the base metal.

Gas-Welded Aluminum Castings

Aluminum castings are generally welded only as a means of repairing foundry defects or to repair castings broken in service. Seldom is welding used in order to assemble units from castings. While there are several methods of welding castings, the most acceptable and the one generally used is the flux and puddling rod process. This involves the use of a steel puddling rod which is essentially a paddle flattened and shaped from a $1/4$ in. round steel rod.

When repairing castings, it is generally found that the base metal lacks the strength and ductility of wrought aluminum and at the same time is defective as well as cracked and dirty. The complicated shape of many castings intensifies shrinkage stresses and increases cracking. All of this makes the welding of aluminum castings a complicated procedure.

Preheating to prevent the spreading of cracks is essential for many castings. Furnace preheating is generally preferred, although in some instances local torch heating may do the job on small castings or for small cracks near the edge and thin sections of large castings. Prior to preheating, it is frequently advisable to drill a hole in the end of the crack in order to prevent it from spreading.

The preheated crack is next coated with a flux. A flux good for sheet aluminum will work quite satisfactorily with castings. The reverse, however, is not true; a flux suitable for aluminum castings may not prove satisfactory in the welding of aluminum sheets. In any event, a satisfactory flux is essential. A puddling rod is needed to weld castings.

When the metal along the edges of the crack becomes mushy under the flame, a vee two or three inches long should be scraped out with the puddling rod. The flux-dipped aluminum welding rod is then melted into the veed section, and either the paddle or the welding rod is used to scrape the bottom and sides of the weld puddle and to level off the top of the mushy weld metal. As soon as one short section is filled another section should be begun. Only the hot fluid weld metal is paddled. The direction of the flame is immaterial as long as the molten material is not being driven over the edges of the bevel.

Welding Magnesium

Magnesium is rapidly becoming an important metal in the field of light metal fabrication. The magnesium alloys now in popular use contain 90% or more magnesium alloyed with aluminum, manganese, zinc, silicon and sometimes tin. Most of these alloys can be fabricated, with varying degrees of success, by oxy-acetylene welding.

Welding Qualities

The welding qualities of magnesium alloys are in many respects quite similar to aluminum in that they have the following common characteristics: High heat conductivity, low melting point and high thermal expansion. There are, however, two important points at which magnesium alloys differ greatly from those of aluminum, they are: (1) the greater likelihood of magnesium alloys to crack during welding and working and (2) the greater need for complete flux removal. Because of this second difference magnesium welds are limited to those of the butt type.

Magnesium alloys of a weldable analyses cannot

be welded to aluminum alloys or to other metals, nor can they be torch cut. These alloys may be obtained in a number of different forms, such as, sand and permanent mold castings, sheets, plates, bars and extruded shapes, and may be welded to one another. The more nearly the pieces approach each other in chemical composition the more rapidly they may be welded.

Joint Preparation

Prior to any magnesium welding operation, the items to be welded should be cleaned thoroughly of all grease, oil or dirt. As a rule steel wool cleaning is satisfactory. To insure complete cleaning, however, a non-corrosive solvent such as a hot alkaline cleaner, naphtha, gasoline or carbon-tetrachloride is often used. As a rule, magnesium alloys are given a corrosion resistant coating by the producer. If this is the case, this protective coating and all traces of oxidation must be removed from the edges of the adjacent surfaces of the pieces to be welded. This careful cleaning and brightening operation may be accomplished with emery cloth, steel wool, files, scrapers or wire brushes.

When castings, forgings or extrusions are to be welded to sheets, the thickness of their sections along the seam junction should be approximately the same thickness as that of the sheets. If not, it will be necessary to preheat the heavier fittings prior to welding so that the two edges of the seam will begin to melt simultaneously. This is a standard welding procedure applicable to the welding of practically all metals as well as magnesium.

Welding Difficulties

In welding magnesium alloy sheets or strips 0.050 in. thick or less, the weld may be of a flange or butt type with the flange type preferred. These flanges must be melted down into a plain butt before the completion of the weld, however, because of the danger of trapping corrosive flux. Up to ⅛ in. all thicknesses are butted for satisfactory welds. Thicker sheets must have the edges to be welded beveled on about 45 deg

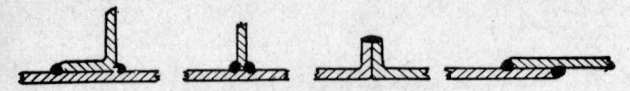

Fig. 4—Welds similar to these are subject to flux inclusions and should not be used in welding magnesium alloys.

and an unchamfered lip, not more than 1/16 in. may be left to insure proper penetration when the material is over ¼ in. thick.

As shown in Fig. 4, there are certain types of joints which must be avoided when welding magnesium alloys. The difficulty experienced in flux removal after weld-

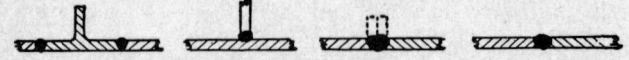

Fig. 5—Welds like these may be thoroughly cleaned without difficulty and are therefore recommended for use in fabricating magnesium alloy structures.

ing makes it unwise to use lap, fillet, plug and in some cases, corner welds. Corner and fillet welds may be permissible if root penetration is complete (See T-welds of Fig. 5.) Care should be taken, however, to see that there will be no closely jointed surfaces or crevices to trap flux.

Flux Important

The use of flux is most important in magnesium welding. Proper use of flux prevents the formation of oxides during welding and also breaks up the oxide films on the metal which would prevent coalescence of filler and parent metal. There are available several commercial fluxes for use when welding magnesium alloys and, in some cases, satisfactory results have been obtained using aluminum flux.

Since these fluxes are usually in powdered form and readily absorb moisture, with a resultant loss in effectiveness, they must be kept in tightly closed containers. The flux is prepared for use in welding by mixing with water until a paste is formed. Only a small quantity, not over a day's supply, should be prepared at one time owing to the loss of efficacy that occurs after mixing and storing.

This paste mixture is applied to the welding rod either by dipping or with a small swab or brush. It

Fig. 6—The cross section of various welds made on magnesium sheets: (1) too much penetration; (2) too little penetration; (3) too heavy reinforcement; (4) correct weld bead and (5) appearance of cross section after cold working and milling.

is usually recommended that the rod be heated to approximately 400 F prior to fluxing in order to obtain a more uniform coating. It is also advisable to apply flux to both surfaces of the pieces to be welded, but particularly the under side of the seam to prevent oxidation of the penetration bead.

Filler Rod

Welding rods of approximately the same chemical composition as the base metal should be used in the welding of magnesium alloys. It is especially important that the rod be the same composition as the sheet when cast or forged fittings are welded to a sheet. While commercial welding rods are produced for all weldable magnesium alloys, if none are available strips of metal cut from sheet may be used.

Like all magnesium alloys, the commercial welding rods are supplied with a corrosion resistant coating which must be removed by wire brushing or with steel wool before using. After a welding operation, all traces of flux should be removed from the unused portion of the rod.

Welding Procedure

Considerable care is necessary to avoid stressing the metal on those parts to be welded in jigs because of the tendency of such parts to crack from expansion or contraction resulting from welding heat. Tight clamping is to be avoided and it should not be necessary because the design of the parts, if proper, is based on allowing full freedom of the parts to expand and contract during the welding operation. It has been found that, in general, the same practice as followed in welding aluminum will be satisfactory except that a greater number of tack welds are required.

In welding magnesium, the oxy-acetylene torch is adjusted and used in a manner similar to that employed on other metals. A neutral or slightly reduced flame is best as it provides a reducing gas envelope about the molten metal. In no case should an oxidizing flame be used.

The flame should be directed on the work at an angle of about 30 deg to the plane of the sheets and in line with the weld seam, thus gradually forcing the molten flux ahead of the weld metal. It is important when welding thin sheets, that the torch angle be kept as flat as possible to prevent holes being burned through the sheets. Magnesium alloys give no color indication of approaching their melting point so extreme care should be taken at the beginning of a weld to avoid burning. Should any portion of the weld become burned, welding must be stopped and the burned area carefully recleaned by scraping or filing.

The seams should be tack welded at intervals of ½ to 2½ in. depending somewhat on the type of joint and thickness of the sheet. Warping and cracking during subsequent welding operations may be reduced to a minimum by first welding toward the ends of the seam for 1 or 2 in. Should the sheets warp during tacking, they should be straightened with a wooden mallet, while hot. The tacked spots are then refluxed and the entire seam welded keeping in mind that starting and stopping of welding must be kept to a minimum. Upon coming to the end of a bead, it is suggested that an excess of metal be deposited at as low a temperature as is possible. This extra metal will help eliminate shrinkage cracks at the end of the bead. If necessary, the sheets are again straightened after welding has been completed. Welded magnesium parts for aircraft are usually left "as welded" but if the specifications call for a finished weld the excess should be removed. The excess weld metal and slag of the completed weld may be removed by chipping or milling followed by hammering if necessary. The weld bead should never be dressed down by hammering alone.

In Fig. 6 is shown the cross section of various welds made on magnesium sheets: (1) too much penetration; (2) too little penetration; (3) too heavy reinforcement; (4) correct weld bead and (5) appearance of cross section after milling and cold working.

Weld Cleaning

After the weld has been completed and has cooled sufficiently to be handled, the weld cleaning operation should be begun. The excess welding flux must be completely removed by vigorously scrubbing the weld bead with a bristle brush and hot water. Washing and soaking should be continued until the surface is clean. *If this is not done promptly serious corrosion will result.* The welded part, when completely cleaned, may then be immersed in a hot anodizing or chrome pickling solution which will produce a chromate coating on the weld affording protecting through its inhibitive character. If the weld is sound no further treatment is necessary.

It should be remembered that much of the success of a weld in magnesium alloys depends upon the effectiveness of the post-weld cleaning and the subsequent corrosion inhibiting treatment.

White Metal

Welding of white metal or die-castings is considered by some to be a difficult or impractical application, probably because of the wide variety of alloys and the range of melting points which exist. Frequent odd shapes and small cross sections offer further difficulties. Such metals fall into about four general groups: aluminum base, zinc base, lead base and tin base, arranged in the order of their approximate melting points. Recently, a good portion of the commonly used alloys follow SAE Specifications 903, 921 and 925. They are largely composed of zinc and aluminum with copper and some other elements added. They have fairly high tensile strengths, but low ductility.

Flame Adjustment

The tip selected for this work should be one or two sizes smaller than is indicated for steel of comparable thickness. The flame should be extremely carburizing with only enough oxygen to form a blue envelope beyond the yellow acetylene flame and sufficient to keep the acetylene flame from sooting the work. With the flame properly adjusted bring the tip up to within ¼ to ½ in. of the fracture until the metal starts to flow. Vee out the metal at the break to an included angle of about 45 deg., using a bronze paddle of proper size. Clean the surface well back of scale, plating, etc.

Making the Weld

With the metal properly heated turn the flame parallel to the surface to hold the metal just at the molten stage. Heat the rod until it is molten and touch te the break. The filler material will flow and fuse thoroughly. This operation is continued until the break is filled. It is a good idea to touch the tip of the rod to the surface of the weld so as to break the surface tension of the molten metal to insure fusion. Welding should be done from one side only or at best a small line of the underside of the fracture should be veed out slightly and welded.

The filler material selected should be one suitable for the work at hand, several of which are available from regular sources of supply. Lacking such materials it is possible to melt up scrap pieces of the same material being worked on and pour into the vee of a piece of angle iron laid level.

Preheating Methods

Since white metal has large expansion and contraction, it may be necessary to preheat some castings, particularly when complicated sections are encountered. A good practice is to place the part on a steel plate ⅜ to ½ in. thick and apply the flame of a preheating torch immediately underneath. When the plate just begins to show red the preheating is sufficient. Another thought to keep in mind when thin sections are en-

192   WELDING PROPERTIES OF COMMON METALS

countered and sagging may occur when heat is applied, is to make a mold or backing plate of thin sheet metal to act as a support.

Flame cutting a laminated steel "burglar-proof" safe is difficult but it can be done.

CHAPTER 10
TESTING WELDS

The subject of testing* is greatly underestimated by the average welding operator who is apt to regard it as based on the lack of confidence in his ability. On the contrary, the subject of testing is introduced to help the operator find ways to check the quality of his own work and to help the supervisor in the welding department to hold the quality of all welds made in the department up to a certain standard, so that there will be no doubt as to how long the welded articles will last when put into service. By passing these simple requirements, the welding operator raises the standard of his profession in the eyes of the engineer and the public.

The discussions of testing which follow will therefore serve a double purpose. In the first place they will suggest to the man in charge of welding operations some of the standard methods used for testing welds and in the second place to show the operator in many cases how he can investigate his own workmanship and compare it with standard results.

Examining the Weldor

A new weldor should never be put to work without a careful examination to make sure that he is properly qualified for the job. Very often it is advisable to give a short oral examination to find out just how much the weldor knows about welding in general and about the specific type of work he is expected to do.

---
*The discussion of testing in this chapter should not be mistaken for weldor qualification where the work being done is under a specific code or specification.

This oral examination should show whether the applicant for the position is thoroughly familiar with the apparatus which he will have to handle and whether he understands what constitutes a good welding job. A good deal can be learned regarding the latter point if a number of samples of good welding and poor welding are available and the applicant is asked to pick out the good work and tell what is the matter with the defective work.

Typical Job Try Out

Such an examination can be followed by putting a complete outfit at the disposal of the applicant and asking him to go to work on a typical job. Notice how he goes about the procedure of getting ready to work; how he handles tanks; whether he takes pains to see that all apparatus and materials are properly disposed for safety; whether he blows out the hose and the torch before making a connection; whether he gets everything ready for the work so that he can proceed with the welding uninterrupted after he gets started.

Tip Selection a Good Gauge

Make particular note of his judgment in selecting the tip for the thickness of metal to be welded. If the tip selected is much too small it shows ignorance of that class of work. If it is much too large it shows a tendency to rush the work for the sake of making a showing. Then notice how closely he follows instructions for the adjustment of pressure according to the size of tip which he has selected, and how carefully he adjusts the flame to make sure of getting it neutral.

Watch Torch Manipulation

As he starts welding, not whether he is able to start at the bottom with complete confidence so that he can get full penetration; and watch the puddle to see whether he carries the fusion along smoothly and uniformly. Note particularly if he has a tendency to go back over his work and reheat it in order to make the work look well on top. It only requires a short demonstration to determine whether the weldor is skillful enough for the work in hand or whether he is so lacking in skill as to require considerably more training before he can be put to work on production, or whether he can be put to work after a few minor mistakes in his method have been corrected.

It is impossible to outline methods of examination covering all possible or even all of the common types of welding operations. It should be a rule, however, that a systematic method of examination be followed with each weldor added to the payroll. The suggestions made above are for the purpose of emphasizing the desirability of testing the weldor and suggesting along what lines he should be tested.

The Tensile Test

There are quite a number of methods of testing welds. The purpose of each separate test is to determine how good the weld is for a particular kind of service. One of the most popular and useful tests is called the tensile test. This determines the resistance of the weld to tensile or pulling action. That is, it indicates the amount of force necessary to pull it apart. Furthermore, it is commonly considered that if a weldor can make a weld which passes a satisfactory tensile test he is a good operator; and for this reason weldors but are also required to weld test coupons at frequent who are working on important welding operations are often not only required to qualify by welding test coupons to be pulled in the tensile testing machine,

intervals while they are on the work, to make sure that they are keeping their workmanship up to the required standard.

Preparation of Specimens

Due to the importance which is attached to the tensile test every weldor should understand just how to go about making welding test specimens. A typical

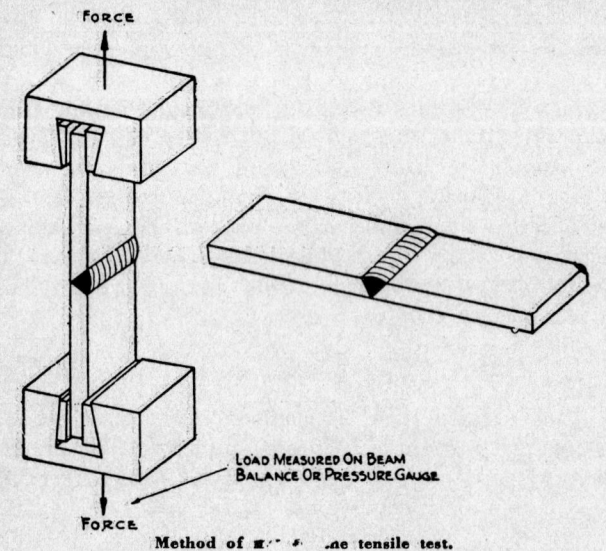

Method of making tensile test.

procedure outlined by the Oxy-Acetylene Committee of the International Acetylene Association is in part as follows:

1. The samples for welding shall consist of two 4 in. by 12 in. mild steel plates ½ in. thick. The weld shall be a single vee butt weld along the 12 in. edge. The first 4 in. of each joint are to be welded in the horizontal plane, the next 4 in. in the vertical

plane, and the remaining 4 in. in the overhead position.

2. The welded specimens shall be cut into nine 8-inch by 1 in. test coupons, three being taken from the center of each 4 in. section. Three of these, one from each position, shall be subjected to the nick-break test, three to the tension test, and three to the free bend test. Any reinforcement of the weld shall first be removed by machining or grinding to thickness of plate material for tension and free bend tests.

Making the Tensile Test

Specimens made up as described above are pulled apart in a tensile testing machine and record made of the ultimate strength, yield point, the reduction of area, and per cent elongation. Comparatively few plants are equipped with the apparatus for making these tests but in practically all locations there are testing laboratories which will test the specimens and make the report for a moderate fee.

Using the Data

Although the tensile test can actually measure only the resistance of the weld to pulling and does not accurately indicate other physical properties of the weld, it is nevertheless true that the tensile test will tell the experienced supervisor a great deal of the quality of the weld itself and of the ability of the operator who made it. It is for this reason that the tensile test is so popular in the welding industry. It has been used so much that some large organizations are accustomed to classify their operators according to the strength shown by tensile specimens which they prepare, a first class weldor being expected to produce welds which will stand 50,000 psi.

It is evident therefore, that any weldor can secure a comparative rating on his own workmanship by welding test coupons and sending them to a good laboratory for examination. In case the results are disappointing the reason for this may be determined by giving the work a thorough examination according to the suggestions made in the chapter on inspecting welds.

Free Bend Test

The free bend test is one which ranks with the tensile test in importance because in general it is the most practical method of measuring the ductility of

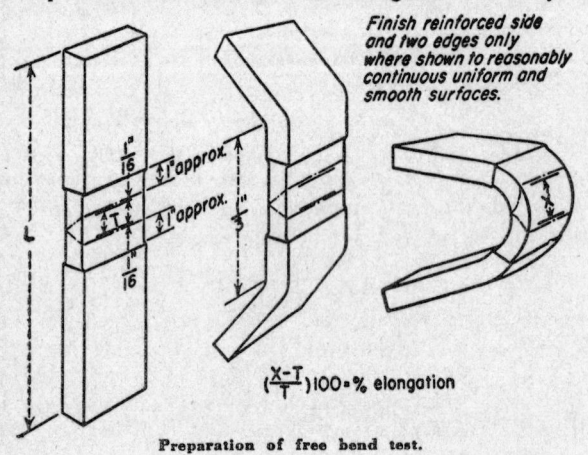

Finish reinforced side and two edges only where shown to reasonably continuous uniform and smooth surfaces.

$(\frac{X-T}{T})100 = \%$ elongation

Preparation of free bend test.

the weld. Lack of ductility is for all practical purposes the same as brittleness, and there are many types of welded structures such as tanks and pipe assemblies in which it is very undesirable to have brittleness present, for the weld may often be called upon to stand bending.

Making the Test

Some rather elaborate bending machines have been devised for making the bend test, but a very satisfactory test can be made with very simple apparatus, that is, with a hammer and vise. This is an important angle from the point of view of the weldor in the average shop because a satisfactory bend test is often just as good an indication of the quality of the weld as the tensile test. The usual amount of reinforcement should be made when welding and this reinforcement ground off before starting to make the test. Then three punch marks are made on a line perpendicular to the direction of the weld, one in the center of the weld and one on each side. The distance between these punch marks should be very accurately measured before the test is started.

The sample is placed in a heavy vise and the ends hammered over slightly in the direction toward the bottom of the weld, leaving the center portion flat for a distance on each side of the weld, just about equal to the width of the weld itself. Now open the vise wide enough so that it will take hold of the whole test piece lengthwise. Gradually close the vise until the weld metal shows the first signs of cracking. At this point the distance between the punch marks on the edges of the weld is accurately measured with a flexible steel scale. This distance, of course, will be longer than the original distance and the fractional increase in this distance is the per cent of elongation.

Welds made with a good quality mild steel rod in a good quality steel plate should show an elongation of between 25 and 30%. One caution must be observed in making this bend test, that is, care must be taken to bend the specimen so that practically all of the bending comes in the weld metal. Otherwise, the test is of no value. It is also observed that the specimen must be bent so that the top of the weld metal is on the outside of the bend. It must be borne in mind that the purpose of this type of bend test is not to find out whether it is possible to break the weld by bending it. The real purpose is to determine the degree of ductility in the deposited metal.

Nick Break Test

The nick break test has been devised as a means of studying a cross sectional area of the weld. It is made with a hammer and either a vise or two heavy blocks across which the specimen is laid as indicated in an accompanying illustration. A quick sharp blow

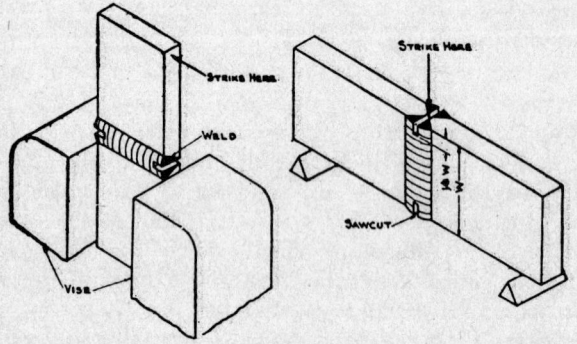

Preparation of nick break specimen and method of use.

with a heavy hammer against the coupon with the notch in tension will break the weld and show very clearly the quality of the deposited metal. The fracture should be examined for poor fusion, laps, porosity, lack of penetration and character of deposited metal. Generally, a weldor is disqualified by this test if as many as eight imperfections appear in the break and none of these defects should have a dimension greater than $1/16$ in.

Of other types of test which are variously required, one is the root bend test in which the specimen is placed on a support with the root of the weld away from the force which is applied to cause fracture. A second is the face bend where the face of the weld must withstand applied force until fracture occurs while another sometimes called for is the side bend test where the side of the weld is treated in the same way.

The tests considered so far have taken into account mainly the physical properties of the weld or the welded structure. Care should be taken in the arrangement of a testing program to make sure that the tests indicate the serviceability of the entire structure as well as the strength of the weld itself. This is because it is quite possible to build up a good, sound, strong deposit of weld metal and still leave points of weakness in some other location which might be avoided by proper design and proper welding procedure.

In the welding of containers, which may be taken to include both tanks and pipes, it is almost always essential that the welds should be leak proof and whenever there is any possibility of loss or damage as the result of a leaky weld. Every weld should be tested for tightness. There are several ways of doing this.

Soapsuds Test

If the amount of welding on a pipe system or tank is comparatively small and the weld is fairly accessible, the soapsuds method is a good test. The procedure is to seal the whole container, leaving a small inlet for compressed air. Then brush a thick soapsuds solution over all the welds and turn on air pressure to about 5 psi pressure. Leaks are quickly located by the formation of bubbles.

Submersion Test

On articles which can be submerged in a tank of water, the submersion test is sometimes quicker than the soapsuds test. It is only necessary to seal the article and completely submerge it in water and turn a little air pressure into it. Bubbles will rise to the surface from any points of leakage.

A common test for leaky welds on large tanks is made with ordinary kerosene. If this is applied freely to one side of a weld, it will soak through any porous spots that may be present.

Etched Specimens

In some cases it is desirable to make a careful examination of the quality of the deposited metal and the quality of the union between the deposited metal and the parent metal. A direct examination can be made by cutting out a specimen, carefully polishing it in the area which it is desired to examine, then etching with a suitable etching fluid. Sometimes an examination of an etched specimen with a small powered microscope or ordinary reading glass gives a satisfactory account of the quality of the metal. Frequently, however, such specimens are turned over to a metallographic laboratory where higher powered microscopes are used to magnify the view of the metal to the point here the nature of the grain structure can be examined and the presence of oxides or slag inclusions determined.

The tests described above are the most common ones in use in large production welding departments. Any one of them or any group of them may be used to the exclusion of the others, as the occasion requires. There are also tests for resistance to torsion and to shearing stress, for hardness, for resistance to abrasive wear, for resistance to heat or corrosion or the action of certain acids, and so on. When these special tests are needed, standard procedures for making them can be obtained from manufacturers of the necessary testing equipment or from engineering school laboratories.

Testing the Program

A discussion of testing would not be complete without a general outline of a program for testing an entire welding operation. Suggestions will therefore be given for analyzing a welding job so as to take into account every important fundamental factor involved in the job. In order to make the purpose of this set of suggestions clear, assume that plans have been made for a welding job and that it is desired to go over the plans to make sure that every precaution has been taken to guarantee a good result.

Look for the Cause

First investigate the materials to be used, including both the material to be welded and the equipment and materials used for welding. On repair work the study of the material to be welded is of more importance than some weldors realize. Suppose a part is broken. Was the break caused by an acciden, the cause of which has not been removed, or by vibration due to a badly worn bearing, or by deterioration of the metal in the whole piece, or by a bent shaft which has not been straightened, or by an overload? In any of these cases, or similar cases, welding may repair the break, but it cannot prevent a recurrence. Therefore welding would be waste effort unless the cause of the rupture could be located and removed. Is the metal itself of good welding quality? Can the piece be restored to its original strength, and if so, what amount of reinforcement will be necessary? If it is a worn part which is to be rebuilt, is it subject to more wear than the manufacturers expected, and in that case would it not be judicious to build it up with a hard facing metal rather than with the metal of which it is made? Or would manganese bronze be better than any of the hard facing materials?

The part to be welded must be studied in order to answer such questions, and particularly the question of the desirability of welding. It is waste effort to weld a part which is so weakened that it will break again in another place, or which will be subjected to more stress than it can stand. Another important question is whether the part has been heat treated to give it certain necessary physical properties. The weld, even though it may have the same composition as the parent metal, will not be the same as the parent metal in this case, unless facilities are available for the correct heat treatment, and heat treatment is an art in itself.

Study the Procedure

If the part is an oil-soaked casting, or is covered with paint or scale, time must be allowed for cleaning, if a clean, sound weld is wanted. If the break is in such a position that cooling may cause it to crack, some method of preheating is necessary, and the materials for preheating are selected according to whether slow or rapid, local or entire preheating will be used. Can the part be welded in place, without dismantling, and if so does the use of an open flame constitute a hazard to property or to workmen?

Investigate Code Requirements

Is the work of such a nature that it is subject to regulation by federal, state, municipal, or insurance authorities?

If so, the necessary permission must be obtained. How about the cost of welding? Is it less than the cost of a new part? If not, is money saved by welding in order to get machinery back in service more quickly? These questions apply to hundreds of repair jobs, and indicates that such jobs are worth investigating, to prevent waste effort.

Production Control

When the job under consideration is one of fabrication, or production, instead of repair, the study of the material to be welded is of even greater importance, first because the selection of material can be controlled, and second because a little care exercised in the selection of the material will in many cases insure a better job and a lower production cost for the desired output, with less waste from spoiled material. For example, all iron and steel sheets are not uniform in their welding quality, even though different pieces may prove to have the same chemical analysis and fairly uniform physical properties. Similarly all pipe stock may not be the same in welding quality. A low degree of weldability will retard the work, will lead to non-uniform welds, and may cause the finished product to be rejected. Small pinholes which do not seriously affect the strength may cause difficulties when the job reaches the finishing department. Some of the corrosion-resisting steels and irons are easily welded and others are very difficult to weld. There may be a difference in the cost of the raw materials, but the factor of weldability may prove that the more expensive material is the more economical for a welded job.

If the welded article is to be made of pure copper, it is essential to use deoxidized copper for the parent metal. If such qualities as hardness, ductility, elasticity, etc., are essential to the product, and are present in the material to be welded, it is essential to determine to what extent these properties will be affected by the heat of welding.

Provide Proper Equipment

Attention should next be given to the equipment and materials with which the welding is to be done. The first step in this direction is to figure out just how many torches, how much filler rod, and how much oxygen and acetylene will be needed in order that the work may proceed without interruption while new materials are requisitioned. On very large operations it is advisable to have a few extra equipments and a plentiful supply of gas in reserve. There is no cause for concern about the quality of carbide, oxygen, or acetylene, as American manufacturers of these items keep the quality up to a uniformly high standard. The torch, however, must be chosen with reasonable care. Nearly all torches are made to be used with tips of several sizes, and it is important to select the tip size best suited for the work in hand. Even if it takes quite a little time to find out what is the best size, that time will be spent profitably.

Good Rod Is Essential

The welding rod ranks in importance with the material to be welded. This subject has been discussed in a previous chapter, where it was noted that the rod need not be of exactly the same material as the parent metal, but that in any event the rod should be tested to show that with it the proper deposit can be made, and that it is of the best welding quality. Cheap wire which is not made especially for welding may cause considerable losses in time and gases.

Inspection of materials should of course include fluxes and accessories, both as to quality and working condition. Hose should be tested for leaks, and goggles for comfort and visibility. Regular periodic tests of the entire equipment keeps down maintenance costs and contributes materially to the efficiency of the welding department.

Design and Preparation

The second factor of the welding operation to be investigated is that of design. Has the right type of weld been specified? Is the right amount of welding and the right amount of reinforcement specified? Is the welding located where it will do the most good, where it will get the least amount of stress in service, and where it is most accessible to the weldor? Has the designer shown just how long, how wide, and how thick each weld must be, and what the tolerances are both above and below? And is the supervisor furnished with a gauge which will enable him to check each weld, if necessary? Is proper preparation for welding specified?

Welding Technique

The third factor in the operation is the welding procedure. This includes the amount of tack welding, and the location of the tacks; if more than one layer of deposited metal is required, the manner of securing perfect fusion between layers; the starting point of each weld and the order of making the welds if there are several involved in a single job; the method of assembly in jigs; the method of preheating and the amount of preheating, if necessary; the same details regarding annealing or normalizing; the selection of the welding method itself, whether forehand, backhand, or still-torch; the average rate at which the welding should proceed for good results; the flame regulation; the gas pressures and the size of filler rod to be used. The procedures for different metals have been given in a previous chapter.

Qualify the Weldor

The fourth factor in the job is the weldor himself. He should be qualified for the job on the basis of his capabilities for that particular job. Methods of qualifications have already been discussed. If they are put into effective use, no trouble will be experienced with what used to be called the "human element" in welding.

Final Testing

The final factor in the job investigation is the testing of the completed work. Intelligent, systematic testing tends to maintain the efficiency of welding operations at the highest level. Make use of the test procedures given in the first part of this chapter. Supplement them by special tests, if possible. All of the best manufactured products are tested. Automobile factories spend millions in testing alone, the tests extending from microscopic measurements of the smallest parts to the most severe service tests of completed machines. Still they need service stations. But testing keeps servicing down to a minimum. Likewise testing will keep weld failures down to a minimum.

It is not desired to give the impression in this chapter that oxy-acetylene welding is unreliable and must be surrounded with extraordinary precautions. On the contrary, it requires no more in the way of precautions than any other welding process or any other manufacturing or fabricating process. Every weld made does not have to be subjected to every imaginable test, and in fact, when the work is properly supervised, and organized according to the principles outlined above; the testing will reveal practically no shortcomings. The fact to be noted is that wherever a welding torch is used there should be someone who knows how to use it properly and how to plan a welding job so that there will be the greatest possibility of a thoroughly satisfactory result.

Welding is used on the railroad to buildup rail ends, crossings and switch points.

CHAPTER 11
IMPORTANT APPLICATIONS

In this small volume it is impossible to outline the many ways in which oxy-acetylene welding is used. There are many important applications, a few of which will be discussed in this chapter. The applications which have been selected are those which most frequently confront the job shop weldor. With the aids that are given it will be possible for him to undertake most of the jobs that will come into his shop.

Tank Welding

The welding of tanks and all forms of containers made of all kinds of metal was one of the earliest and continues to be one of the most important applications of oxy-actylene welding. The weldor should not expect any brief discussion to cover all of the subjects which could be covered under this heading. Tanks are made by welding for holding all kinds of liquids and gases, and vary in size from tanks small enough to put into the pocket to huge storage tanks, and, according to the requirements of the container, may be made out of any of the common metals and alloys.

Study the Use

The one important consideration in tank welding is the purpose of the tank itself. That purpose is to hold liquids of all kinds in a specific place. The first requirement is therefore that it be absolutely leakproof, because, depending on the material which the tank is to hold in a confined space, a leaky seam may result in either loss or damage, or both. The next and probably equally important consideration is that of strength. Every container must be so constructed as to be not only leak-proof but also strong enough that there is no danger of its rupturing in the course of normal service. It might appear at first sight that theoretically the welded seam in a tank must be fully as strong as the material in the tank. This is not always a positive requirement because very often the body of the tank is several times as strong as it needs to be and if the welded seam is reasonably close to the parent metal in strength it will last as long as the tank.

It is perfectly feasible to make the welded seam the strongest portion of the tank either by using a special filler material which makes the deposit stronger than the parent metal or by reinforcing the weld so as to make it the strongest part of the structure. This is a sensible way to go about the production of welded tanks, because if special effort is made to secure extra strength, there should be no weld failures when tanks are submitted to test.

Welding Hints

The experience of many welded tank manufacturers point to a number of suggestions which will be found useful in any tank shop. It is generally considered that the butt weld on longitudinal and circumferential seams is the strongest type of weld. The edges of the plate should be prepared by beveling in order to insure perfect penetration. One quarter inch plate is usually beveled from one side only, but on greater thicknesses it is best to get a stronger job by beveling from both sides whenever it is possible to do the welding from both sides. In the latter case it is advantageous to arrange a setup which will allow working upward and have both the inside and outside weld made at the same time.

Very long tanks, made up of several sections welded end to end, should be assembled so that the longitudinal welds in the various sections are staggered, and do not form one continuous line. When making the longitudinal welds it is best to separate the edges at the end opposite the starting point a distance equal to the thickness of the plate multiplied by the number of feet in the length of the seam. The circumferential weld is started by tacking the parts together in enough places to hold the parts firmly in place. In some cases it is possible to roll the cylinder after the longitudinal seam has been finished. This is quite an advantage because it rolls out all flat spots left at the first rolling.

When a number of fittings have to be attached to metal, it is quite an advantage to hold the shell in a jig for welding. The jig serves the double purpose of helping to compensate for expansion and conducting away excess heat which would otherwise get into the parent metal and cause additional buckling. If the plate is galvanized a blower system should be used to draw all the smoke and fumes from the welding so that the operator will not breathe them.

When a number of fittings have to be attached to the tank, these can be attached without causing buckling by brazing them on instead of welding. If the plate is very heavy it is well to follow the welding operation by heating the metal a few inches on each side of the weld to a dull red. This is particularly helpful when the tank is made of high quality metal which has high tensile strength.

Material and Design

Good material for tank welding will show an analysis 0.15 - 20% carbon, 0.60% manganese, 0.50% sulphur, 0.04% phosphorous with tensile strength ranging from 55,000 to 65,000 psi and a yield point of about 30,000

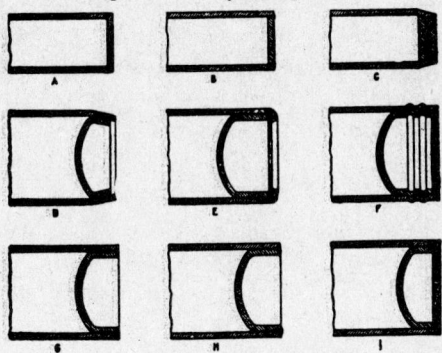

Fig. 1—Heads for small tanks.

psi. The tanks must be designed so as to make the welding as simple and comfortable as possible for the operator, at the same time placing the welding in such a position that it will receive the least amount of stress. Corner welds, for example, should be avoided in the construction of tanks for high pressure service. Heavy duty tanks are often straightened by reinforcing with iron strips around the tops and also by welding stiffener rods from side to side. Before designing a tank it is of course necessary to determine for what use it is intended. Then determine whether there are any regulations concerning the fabrication of tanks for that service and see that the design conforms thoroughly to any existing regulations.

When welding long seams it is necessary to use clamps and wedges to keep the plates in alignment and adjustment. This not only prevents an uneven distribution of stresses but is the only way to get a neat looking job. It must be kept in mind too that pressure tanks are subjected to a breathing action in service, as the pressures change. For this reason the shells on pressure tanks must be rolled to a true circular shape so that after the welding is completed there are no flat sections adjacent to the weld. If such a flat section does exist the changing pressures will tend to swell it out evenly so that there is a continuous alternating bending action on the weld itself.

Design to Use

Some designs for heads of tanks are shown in the chapter on preparation for welding. Figs. 1 and 2 show suggested designs for heads in small tanks and large tanks respectively. The design recommended for large circular tanks is the butt welded dished head indicated in Figs. N to R in Fig. 2, locating the bend an appreciable distance from the weld so that all bending stresses are located in unwelded metal. When it is necessary to weld a patch of new metal to close up a hole in a steel tank, a dished patch should be used and the welding flame should be played on the convex portion of the patch while the weld is cooling, at the same time hammering it lightly until it is even with the rest of the tank.

Weldors who do a considerable volume of small tank work should keep a supply of rollers, clamps and wedges on hand so that a good set up can be arranged for each job. Whenever a number of tanks of the same sort are to be built much time can be saved and more uniform quality in the work be done by the construction of special jigs to hold the material so that the weldors can work conveniently and comfortably.

Pipe Welding

The welding of metal pipe is a type of job for which every welding operator should be prepared. There is so much pipe welding being done that some weldors specialize on this work exclusively and there are some shops which practically make a specialty of welding pipes into various kinds of assemblies. Long pipe lines for carrying oil, gas and water are

Fig. 2—Heads for large tanks.

constantly being constructed, some of them hundreds of miles in length. These lines go over prairies and deserts, through swamps, across rivers and mountains and are laid under all kinds of climatic conditions from the hottest tropical heat to the coldest season in the winter. Obviously the job of welding pipe is not confined to any range of pipe size or to any particular local conditions.

Preparation and Tacking

Most of the pipe welding done is on steel or wrought iron pipe. In order to make a good pipe joint it is essential that the edges be beveled the same as for steel plates. When two lengths are lined up for welding, they should be clamped securely in alignment and held in alignment while they are tack welded together at three or four points depending on the diameter of the pipe. It is desirable to arrange the welding so that the pipe can be turned as the welding progresses, as this eliminates the necessity for overhead welding on the bottom portion of the joint. Overhead welding can be done with perfect satisfaction, but it is more difficult for the operator and consequently requires a little more time.

Welding Technique

Welding on a pipe joint (Fig. 3) should begin at the bottom of one of the top quadrants and be carried over the top to the half-way point and when this is finished the pipe should be turned so as to bring the other half into position for welding. This procedure has the advantage of keeping the weld in such a posi-

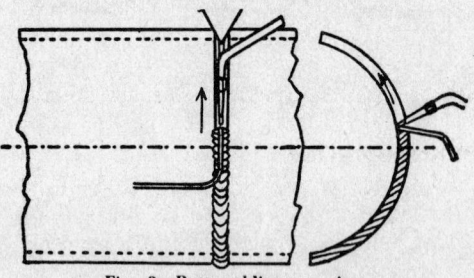

Fig. 3—Butt welding on pipe.

tion that it is easy to get complete penetration without melting through and without danger of the molten metal running away. When the end of the second portion of the joint welded reaches the beginning of the first portion welded, the melting should be carried along for ½ in. or so to make sure that each portion of the weld fuses thoroughly with the adjacent portions. Also when the weld crosses one of the tack welds which has been made to hold the pipe in alignment, the operator should melt completely through the tack weld so as to be sure that his puddle reaches completely to the bottom.

Things to Avoid

The common mistake made by beginners in pipe welding is holding the pool too long in one place while they try to work the surface of the weld into a satisfactory appearance. Another comomn mistake is known as undercutting, that is, failure to build up the weld to its correct dimensions on both sides of the seam. The only way to avoid this is to acquire skill in distributing the heat and the welding rod evenly across the line of weld. Sometimes the beginner is put to work tacking sections together for the more experienced weldors to finish. He may make the mistake of setting the ends of the pipe too closely together so that there is no opportunity for movement due to expansion and contraction of the metal, and this makes trouble for the weldor.

Pipe Line Welding

Long pipe lines are welded as a rule by crews which are very carefully organized. Most of the weldors are kept at work making ordinary butt welds on pipe which can be turned as the welding progresses. There is a limit to the length of pipe which can be turned easily in this way and occasionaly change of direction makes it impossible to turn the pipe. Therefore, a few very skilled weldors are kept "tieing in" the long welded sections. The tieing in weld is often made with pipe line in the ditch. It is not a very comfortable operation and requires a skillful operator. He starts welding at the very bottom of the joint, keeping the flame vertical and holding the rod just ahead of the torch tip. By the time the weld has reached halfway up the pipe he is able to incline the heat of the torch so that the flame is nearly tangent to the surface of the pipe. After he has reached the top he starts again at the bottom going back about $\frac{1}{2}$ inch over the beginning of his first weld to make sure of getting continuous fusion and proceeding up around the pipe to the top where he again melts over $\frac{1}{2}$ in. of the end of his first weld.

Organizing the Work

An elaborate pipe line job requires three groups of weldors: First, the welding crew consisting of four weldors whose job it is to join five 40 ft lengths of pipe. These are followed by tie-up weldors who join two of these 200 ft lengths of pipe. Finally the 400 ft lengths of pipe are joined to the main line by the "bell-hole" weldors. With this type of organization one acetylene generator with a supply of oxygen tanks will serve each welding crew and one man should be assigned to the job of taking care of the generator. Unless a good water supply is available a 250-gallon tank wagon should be supplied for each two generators, as plenty of water will be needed both in the generator itself and for cleaning the generators between charges. Enough clamps should be available so that helpers can go ahead with them and clamp the pipe in position for tacking before the weldors arrive at the joints. The clamps can be removed as the tacking is finished, and sent ahead of the crew

Use Correct Procedure

Experienced supervisors have noted that there is very little trouble from leaking welds in pipe lines if the weldors are careful to use a neutral flame and fuse the metal carefully on both sides of the joint. Many instances in fact have been reported where thousands of welds were made on a single job without finding any leaks whatever. If test coupons are cut from the pipe and tested for strength, any defect in strength is generally traceable to the failure to penetrate to the bottom. If the procedure recommended above for welding pipe is followed, there should be no lack of penetration.

Angles and Branches

One of the important problems involved in pipe welding is in making joints in odd angles for going around corners and welding in branch connections. The solution of the main part of this problem consists in obtaining a template which will make it possible to trace out on the pipe the exact line of cut which will give a perfect fit. After welding a fitting or connection, it is a good plan to heat a small band around the pipe, the width being about one-half of the diameter of the pipe and the heat distributed as evenly as possible.

Wrinkle Bends

Another method which finds frequent use in making bends in pipe is that known as wrinkle bending. It is desirable, for it eliminates the need for carrying templates, marking out the cut, cutting the pipe, and finally making the weld between the sections. Almost any size pipe encountered in the field can be handled by this means.

For pipe six inches and under the use of one torch is sufficient, but on diameters greater than six inches, two torches are recommended. The torch should be of a size large enough to provide ample heat. If two torches are used the operators stand one on each side of the pipe and heat a band two or three inches wide to a red heat. The pipe is then bent by allowing it to sag into the ditch, pulling it horizontally around a post or tree. For small sizes the helper may be able to do the pulling, but on larger sizes a tractor is usually necessary and available on field jobs.

The pipe is upset or wrinkled toward the inside of the bend at the heated section. Recommended practice indicates that each bend should not be made greater than 7 deg., for a bend of greater degree is apt to crush the wrinkle forcing it in as well as out. Successive wrinkles are made until the required degree of bend is obtained. An advantage of this procedure is that the inside diameter of the pipe is not reduced as all the wrinkles extend outward and the wall thickness of the pipe is not decreased.

Welded Headers

The problem of making branch connections is complicated somewhat when a number of small branches are welded onto a large piece fairly close together, forming a header. The main factors involved in welding headers are, first, getting a perfect fit, second, getting penetration without having the molten metal coming through and forming icicles inside the pipe and third, maintaining alignment. There will be no difficulty in getting a perfect fit if a properly designed template is used to mark off the line of cut on both the main line and branch line welded to it. Instructions for making these templates are to be found in any good book on pattern making. A number of sets of curves have been made up covering some of the common pipe connections and can be purchased in complete sets. It is also possible to have these patterns made up in a sheet metal shop where the principles of pattern making are well understood. The second difficulty mentioned, that of having the metal flow through inside of the pipe, is altogether a matter of the skill of the operator. After learning how to get thorough penetration on flat plate it is not very difficult to master the knack of getting the same penetration on pipe connections without melting through.

Maintaining Alignment

The problem of alignment is a little more difficult, particularly if there are several connections to be made to one main. There are several methods of taking care of this difficulty. One method is to let the welding distort the header without taking any precautions against it and then after it is welded turn it upside down and apply to the areas opposite each branch about the same amount of heat that was used in welding the branch. Another method is to keep a fire underneath the main pipe while the connections are being welded. This usually results in a straight job but is rather hard on the operator. A third method is to use a clamp or a set of clamps to bend the main pipe in the direction opposite to that which would be produced by welding, then let the welding operation bring it back again. In case difficulty is encountered in having the branches perpendicular to the main pipe after welding, this can be overcome by starting the weld with the branch pipe or nipple slightly away from the vertical, particularly if location of the connection is close to a head or a flange. The inclination of the nipple should be toward the head or flange and the welding should be started at the point farthest away from the head or flange and carried continuously around to a starting point. In the case of comparatively small diameter headers which do not have to be finished to absolutely accurate dimensions, straightening can be accomplished by heating between the branch connections and bending.

Sheet Metal Welding

Practically all sheet metal articles can be welded by the oxy-acetylene flame and there is probably no article made of sheet metal which is not fabricated in most shops by welding. Some of the principal products are steel furniture, steel building materials, such as doors, door frames and window frames, steel tanks, automobile bodies and cabinets.

Because sheet metal is so light and so easy to bend and also because of the great strength of sheet metal and articles when properly designed, the latter are often subjected to great abuse when put into service. Therefore, it is almost always necessary in the welding of sheet metal articles to make the weld as strong as the rest of the sheet, since any weak spot is apt to be the point of failure in case the finished product is given more than usual service.

The Use of Jigs

The reader will probably recall that a considerable amount of instruction has been given in previous chapters concerning the welding of sheet steel, with particular reference to exercises for beginners and methods of testing the beginner. When these first exercises are examined it will be found that one of the principal defects of the beginner is the distortion which may be either a general bending or a miscellaneous collection of buckled areas. In production work, no better method has been found of overcoming this trouble than the use of jigs. These serve to absorb

of production, but where there is occasion for real mass production to extend over a considerable period, a good deal of the heat of welding and thus confine the heat in the sheet metal to a relatively small space near the line of the weld. A fairly simple jig can easily be constructed of I-beams and bar iron for work on which there is not apt to be a large amount, the economies realized on the proper set up easily justify the expense of providing more elaborate and more efficient holding devices.

Jigs and Design

It should be noted that the use of such devices make it possible to use the butt weld design. It may be easier to set up the work for a lap weld but it is very difficult to get a good looking job and almost out of the question to get a uniformly good weld with that design. If the welds are very short and a neat job is required, it will help to make a cast iron form to put underneath the weld and clamp over the weld a cast iron plate which has been slotted to leave room to get at the seam.

Obtaining a Smooth Finish

There are two ways to get a very smooth finish. One is to weld from the inside, making sure to get complete penetration. The amount of weld material to be ground off is then very small. Another method is to use the "swish" weld which has been described in the chapter on methods of welding. This also leaves very little grinding, but the weldor who uses it must be careful to see that he does not concentrate all his attention on the matter of getting a good finish while he sacrifices the very essential quality of penetration.

Welding Technique

As the thickness of the metal welded decreases, the selection of the proper tip and the adjustment of the gas pressures become more and more important on account of the fact that the thin metals are so easily buckled when too much heat is used. Another important point in the welding of very thin metal is that special care needs to be taken to have the edges clean before starting to weld. What would be a very thin coating of dirt, scale or oxide on thicker plate, and probably give very little trouble to the weldor, represents a very much higher percentage of impurities when the parent metal becomes thinner, so the chance of having dirty metal in the weld is very much increased unless extra care is used in cleaning it.

Aircraft Welding

The use of mild steel or alloy steel tubing for the construction of the fuselage, landing gears, motor mounts, and the assembly of these important parts by welding is standard practice in connection with the present day manufacture of the aircraft. Not only has there been no report of any accident or mishap due to failure of a welded joint on an airplane but a study of the industry concerned shows that welded joints have proved to be a desired element of safety when mishaps occurred from other causes. This perfect record of service is such a wonderful testimonial to the value of the oxy-acetylene welded joint that every user of the process should consider the reason why it has been used with such outstanding success in a field where safety and reliability of construction are factors of the greatest importance.

Probably the chief reason is that welded joints have not been adopted and procedures have not been approved for production work until they have been examined in the minutest details by competent engineers. The extensive use of welding on aircraft work is a development which followed the scientific organization of welding operations in many large industrial plants. Consequently, when the aircraft industry was ready

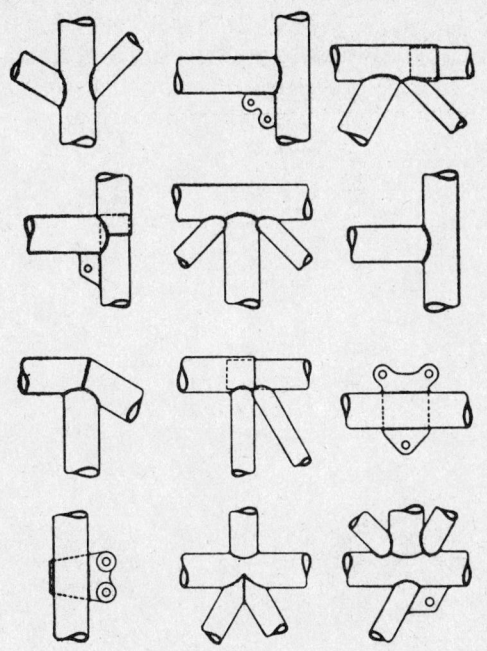

Fig. 4—Typical connections in aircraft assembly.

to use welding there were men available who were able to point out the methods of organizing and conducting welding operations on a truly scientific basis. It is because no pains were spared by this new industry in making arrangements to assure only good welds that their success with it has been so uniform.

Types of Welded Joints

The construction of an airplane usually involves a great many different types of welds (Fig. 4), in a number of different metals and alloys, and different parts of the whole structure, including the power plant. However, the work which is truly typical of aircraft construction is the welding of thin walled tubing such as is used in the fuselage. The serviceability of the completed structure depends to a large extent of course, upon the design of the joints, but this is subject to regulation by the government so the problem of the weldor is one of securing the best possible weld.

Jigs Are Important

All airplane manufacturers know that the construction of jigs for holding the tubes in place for assembly is an indispensable part of the process. So there is this much to help the weldor in his work. The prime consideration is to provide a sufficiently long seam so that the material adjacent to the weld will not be stressed beyond the strength of the parent metal, and also to deposit the material in such a way that there is no under-cutting at any point, that is, no point where the thickness of the tubing is reduced. The weldor must be sure his metal is clean before starting and when welding must be conscientious about securing full penetration even though some of the weld material goes through on the inside, regardless of the outside appearance of the work. (As a matter of fact there is little difficulty in welding a good smooth looking deposit on metal of the thickness used in airplane construction.)

Preparation and Welding

For an ordinary butt weld between two pieces of tubing the end should be square and the tubing clean both inside and outside in the vicinity of the weld. The two pieces should be secured in position by three tack welds which need be only about 1/4 in. long. Whenever possible this type of joint should be rotated while welding as this makes it easier to secure full penetration. The recommended reinforcement is from 1/16 to 1/8 in. on a wall thickness of 0.058 inch. A square cut edge can also be used for a butt welded longitudinal seam. This should be tacked in position and whenever possible held in a jig or clamp so that the welding is done vertically from the bottom upwards. In making a fillet weld best results can probably be secured if the parts are held so that the weld is in a horizontal position, tacking and reinforcing as in the other cases mentioned, and exercising special care that penetration extends to the very bottom of the fillet. When welds are made at tube intersections great care must be used to be sure that they fit as accurately as possible. In all of these cases the contour of the weld should be inspected to be sure that the reinforcement tapers off evenly to the parent metal. In all cases where tack welds are used the operator must be careful to melt completely through the tack when he comes along with the final weld. The reader should go over the section on chrome-molybdenum.

Oxy-Acetylene Brazing

Brazing is a term applied in a general way to joining various metals, using a copper alloy to make the bond. This has sometimes been referred to as hard soldering. There is also included in this general term the process known as welding with bronze. Brazing has long been recognized as a manufacturing process. It consists in using brass spelter or brazing wire to unite parts which have been brought to a sufficiently high temperature. There are a number of methods of production brazing. One is to apply the brazing material in the form of a wire in the same way that the filler material is applied in an ordinary welding operation, with the exception that the parent metal is brought only to red heat and not thoroughly melted. Another method is to have the spelter in the form of filings mixed with flux and applied to the joint which is then heated to the brazing temperature. The third method is to have the spelter in a molten condition in a large container and dip the joint in it. This is called dip brazing. All of these operations are practically soldering operations, the difference being that the brazing spelter makes a much stronger joint. They differ from welding operations in that the parts to be brazed are fitted closely together and the heat is confined to the parts to be brazed as closely as possible. If a good flux is used the spelter will penetrate no matter how tight the joint.

Brazing Malleable

Brazing has long been used for the repair of malleable castings, a bronze welding wire being used in this case. As in production brazing, the parts are fitted tightly together after they have been cleaned as thoroughly as possible. The parts to be joined in this manner should not be heated more than a cherry red. If a manganese bronze welding rod is used a somewhat lower temperature is necessary and this reduces the effect of the heat on the malleable casting.

Silver Brazing

Silver brazing, sometimes called hard soldering, is carried on with various alloys of which there are two general analyses in use. They flow freely, penetrate well, are corrosion resistant and make strong joints that withstand vibration and severe shocks very well. All ferrous and non-ferrous metals and their alloys lend themselves to this type of fabrication with the exception of those with low melting points such as aluminum and zinc. Melting points range from about 1200-1600 F. This temperature range is important when working with metals which are hot-short within the welding range or which may be subject to carbide precipitation. Joints with strengths up to 60,000 psi. are possible.

Brazing Alloys

One of the general types in use is made up of silver and varying amounts of other metals, particularly copper and zinc. The different combinations account for the range of melting points and also variations in color which is often an important consideration. Another type is an alloy of copper and phosphorous melting at about 1300 F. The phosphorous makes possible the low melting point and also acts as a fluxing agent. This type should be used for joints in copper, brass and bronze.

Cleaning the Joint

The first important consideration in preparing the work is cleaning. The areas to be joined must be

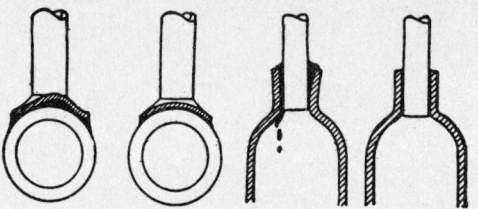

Good and bad joint preparation for silver brazing.

thoroughly cleaned of grease, oxide, scale or other foreign matter of any kind. Any of the accepted methods may be used such as chemical cleaning (which must be carefully washed off and parts dried), smooth cut filing, emery cloth polishing or grinding with a fine grit wheel. Cleanliness is an absolute essential.

Preparation and Jigs

In preparing the joint, it is well to remember that silver brazing alloys will penetrate very narrow openings. Experience indicates that an opening of only 0.002-0.003 in. is required to make the strongest joint; for example, in tubing where one part fits into another. In fact, larger openings or gaps only add to the expense of the job and do not add any strength. A drive fit, on the other hand is not desirable. When the work is being prepared thought should be given to a means of holding it in place while the deposit is being made. The parts when set up should be held firmly while the silver brazing alloy is being applied and kept there until the alloy has thoroughly hardened. For production work, where many parts are to be made over and over, a suitable jig will speed up the operation and insure a low percentage of rejects. In making such a fixture thought should be given to ease of assembling the parts and unloading the finished work and also of locating the joint in the jig so that the operator can easily reach all sides of the joint with the flame.

Where the job at hand is not of a repetitive nature a jig may not be warranted. In such cases, it is an easy matter to arrange a combination of C-clamps, angle irons, bars, etc., so that the parts are held firmly in position.

Application of Flux

If a silver brazing alloy is used, the use of a good flux is essential to prevent oxidation of the metals when the heat is applied and also to dissolve any existing oxides which may not have been removed. Borax or mixtures of borax and boric acid are good preparations to use, but it is not recommended that the operator attempt to make up his own. Rather, as in the case of selecting the alloy, buy one from an accepted source of supply which can furnish material which is particularly adapted to the work. The best method of application is to brush on a solution of the flux, working it in both directions so that no exposed areas remain. Any bare spots will oxidize before the flux melts after heat is applied. It is also a good idea to apply a coating of flux to the silver alloy itself.

Torch Technique

Use a soft neutral flame. Any deviation should be only mildly on the carburizing side. Heat the joint and surrounding metal slowly before applying the alloy always keeping the torch in motion. Apply the brazing alloy when the metal in the joint shows a dull red. Another method of judging the proper temperature is to observe the flux when the flame is momentarily removed from the joint. If it remains fluid, the silver alloy may be applied. In applying the brazing alloy, it is well to let the stored up heat of the parent metal flow the alloy into the joint. If the brazing alloy tends to "ball," the joint has been improperly cleaned, improperly fluxed and either overheated or underheated. When joining dissimilar metals or those of different thicknesses, more heat should be applied to that which is the more rapid conductor of heat on the one hand or to that which has the thicker section on the other. Carry the heat well back from the joint in both cases.

In general, silver brazing should be done in a room free from drafts. The operator should not face the light. In fact, a northern exposure with the light coming from the operator's back is ideal, for it permits him to make critical observation of color changes in the metals as they heat. Other conditions most apt to cause trouble are dirty surfaces, improper application of flux and poor fit-up.

Hard Facing

Some articles made of metal are subjected to extremely hard wear in service. Such parts include metal cutting tools, oil well drilling tools, grinding, crushing and conveying equipment, excavating equipment and some machinery parts. These articles are often made of alloy steels, classified as high carbon steel, manganese steel or high speed steel. These materials are very hard and very resistant to wear but still they wear out in service. Many materials have been produced which show very great resistance to wear but are so expensive that the cost of making an entire machine tool, dipper tooth, or oil well drill bit, from any of them would be prohibitive. Methods have therefore been devised for adding these extra hard materials to iron or steel bases so that only enough of the hard material is used to take up the wearing or abrasive action required by the service of the part. This operation is called hard facing.

Types and Methods of Application

There are several hard facing materials used which vary in composition and in physical properties and are applied in different ways to other base metals. Sometimes a thin layer is flowed on in much the same way that the tinning layer of bronze is applied to cast iron, avoiding the melting of the base metal as much as possible. Others are fused solidly with the base metal, although the penetration is held to a minimum. There are other metals of extreme hardness which are applied to the base metal by carefully setting them in a deposit of high carbon steel or other suitable filler material. Each of the hard facing materials which can be applied by welding have been carefully studied from this point of view in a laboratory. Therefore, when any such material is used the weldor should obtain specific instructions for welding which are supplied by the manufacturer of that material.

These materials can be used for the repair of a great many kinds of equipment and machinery. They can also be used extensively in production as it is obviously better to manufacture a tool or machine part, with the right material already applied to the wearing surface, than to make it out of inferior metals and wait for it to wear out.

Oxy-LP Gas Heating and Brazing

When LP Gas is substituted for acetylene the proportions of oxygen to LP Gas can be adjusted to produce an inner cone which is approximately two times the length of the shortest cone possible. At this adjustment the flame temperature will be approximately 4600 F and will burn three volumes of oxygen for each volume of LP Gas consumed.

This flame temperature is lower than that produced by oxyacetylene and therefore offers advantages in some types of bronze welding, silver brazing and in preheating of certain metals.

The weldor should clearly understand, however, that *oxy-LP Gas is* **not** *satisfactory for the fusion welding of iron and steel* because of this lower flame temperature. Further, if the oxygen adjustment is increased to raise the flame temperature to a welding heat, a highly oxidizing flame will result which will burn iron or steel and render the metal worthless.

CHAPTER 12
OXYGEN - FUEL GAS CUTTING

The rapid cutting of iron and steel is one of the most valuable uses to which the oxy-acetylene flame is put in industry. The operation of oxy-acetylene cutting is based upon the affinity of oxygen for iron, that is, the fact that oxygen combines readily with iron to form iron oxide. It is well known that both iron and steel will rust if exposed to atmosphere or left in contact with water. This rusting is a slow oxidation process. However, if the metal is raised to a white heat and then a good supply of oxygen turned on, the oxidizing process will be much more rapid. In fact the metal will burn just as paper or wood will burn in the atmosphere. The cutting process is therefore, a matter of actually burning through a section of steel or iron, and while an entire piece of such metal could be consumed in this way the general practice is to localize the action and carry it along a definite path to produce what is commonly referred to as a cut.

The Cutting Torch

The tool used for cutting is called the cutting torch. This torch differs from the welding torch in two important respects. It has the regular oxygen and acetylene inlets and a mixing chamber for mixing the two gases, a passage from the mixer to the tip of the torch where the oxy-acetylene flame, similar to that used in welding, is produced. In addition to this, however, there is an extra oxygen passage controlled by a valve and delivering an extra supply of pure oxygen to the tip and so controlled by the extra valve that the extra oxygen supply can be shut off while the oxy-acetylene flame, which in the case of the cutting torch is known as the preheating flame, is being adjusted.

There is also a difference in the tip used. Instead of having a single hole in the center, the tip has one large hole in the center and several smaller holes around it. It is through these smaller holes that the oxy-acetylene flame is produced so that the tip in reality produces a number of small oxy-acetylene flames. The hole in the center is the outlet provided for the extra supply of oxygen and it should be noted that no acetylene is mixed with the oxygen in this central passage. The oxygen delivered through this passage is commonly referred to as the cutting jet of oxygen.

Using the Cutting Torch

The method of using the oxy-acetylene cutting torch is not at all complicated. In fact it is so extremely simple that many cutting operations can be satisfactorily performed by unskilled workmen with only a brief period of instruction. (Many types of cutting work are so important, however, that it is desirable to use men who are both experienced and very skillful in handling the cutting torch.) Careful training in the fundamentals of economical oxy-acetylene cutting is also very desirable on large cutting operations where skillful operators can greatly reduce the time and gas consumption by following the proper procedure.

Assembling the Cutting Torch

The welding tip assembly must be removed from the torch handle body so that the cutting attachment may be secured to the torch handle. This is made easy by the two torch wrenches, one of which is furnished with the welding outfit and the other with the cutting attachment. Engage the throat of the torch head with one wrench and the connector nut on the cutting attachment with the other wrench. Now squeeze them together in a scissors fashion (Fig. 1).

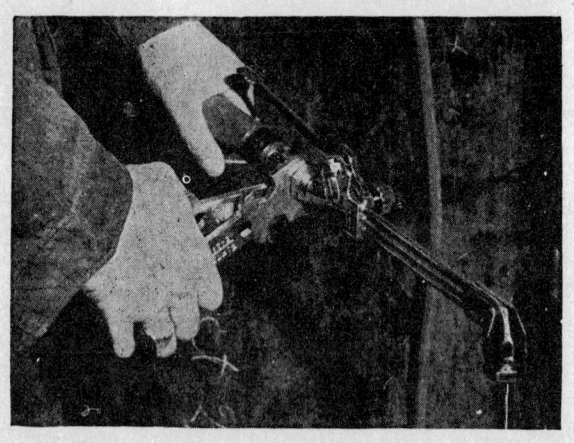

Fig. 1—Tighten the cutting attachment head to torch handle using the two wrenches in a "scissors fashion."

Having tightened the attachment, blow out the attachment head by momentarily squeezing the high pressure oxygen cutting lever. Do this before inserting or changing tips to guard against damaging the tip seat by particles of rust, dust or other foreign material. Insert the tip and secure with tip nut (Fig. 2), using a torch wrench. Tighten the nut snugly but not with excessive force. The essential parts of the oxy-acetylene cutting attachments are shown in Fig. 3. It should be remembered that a cutting attachment can be used only with a welding torch handle of the same manufacture.

Use Care in Arrangement

The first step in a cutting operation is to see that material to be cut is so disposed that there is no danger of injury to the operator or to other workmen

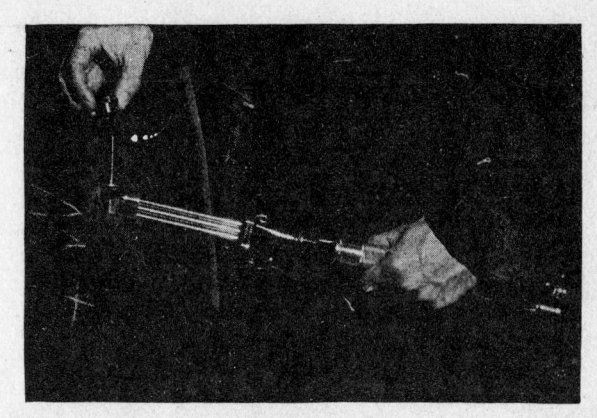

Fig. 2—Place the proper size tip in the cutting attachment, then secure with tip nut.

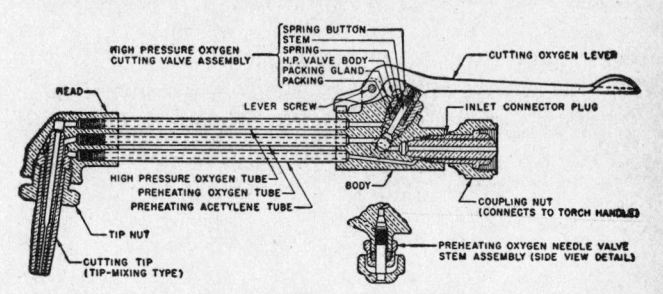

Fig. 3—Essential parts of the oxy-acetylene cutting attachment for use only with welding torch handle of same manufacture.

or to property either from the hot slag which flows out of the cut or as a result of dropping either of the cut sections; that the equipment be stationed where it will not be liable to be injured from any of these causes, particular attention being paid to placing the hose so that there is no chance for hot slag to drop on it. Then the line of cut is marked carefully on the metal, preferably using a sharp piece of soapstone. Chalk is not desirable because the flame will remove it almost instantly from the surface of the metal for a considerable distance. On work where great accuracy is required it is also well to mark the line with punch marks made with a center punch.

Starting the Cut

With these preparations made the operator lights the torch and adjusts the preheating flame to neutral, just as for welding. This flame is held on the spot where the cut is to begin until the small spot on the metal is nearly white hot. Then the torch tip is withdrawn about $1/8$ in. and the cutting oxygen valve is opened gradually. The process of oxidation takes place immediately so a small nick is opened underneath the torch tip. The heat generated by the oxidation of the metal aided by the heat of the preheating flame raises the temperature of adjacent metal sufficiently so that by holding the cutting oxygen valve open and moving the tip gradually along the line of cut the process continues until the end of the line of cut is reached.

Gas Pressures Important

It should be noted carefully that while oxy-acetylene cutting appears to be a melting and blowing procedure, when one observes it in operation, it is in reality a chemical process. The rate of cutting therefore depends upon the selection of a preheating flame of the correct capacity and the adjustment of the cutting jet of oxygen so that this oxygen is supplied in just the right amount to combine thoroughly with the amount of metal which must be consumed in making the cut.

Watch Rate of Cutting

Of course another consideration is the rate of advance of the cutting flame. If the torch is moved too rapidly, the metal does not have a chance to get properly heated, so that it will unite readily with the cutting oxygen. In this case the cutting stops and the metal must be heated again with the preheating flame in order to make a new start. If the torch moves too slowly the oxygen has time to combine with the metal on both sides of the kerf (the slot made by cutting) as well as the metal directly ahead. The result is a kerf much wider than necessary and involving a considerable waste of the cutting gases.

Select Tip from Chart

One essential in efficient and economical cutting is the selection of the proper tip size for the thickness of metal to be cut and the correct adjustment of pressure of both oxygen and acetylene for the tip size used. All manufacturers of cutting torches conduct extensive experiments with their torches to determine which tip size is best suited for definite thicknesses of metal and what pressure of acetylene and oxygen are to be recommended for each individual tip size. This information is furnished in chart form and the operator should develop a technique which will enable him to get satisfactory speed for cutting with the tip size and pressures which are recommended. These recommendations are usually based on the cutting of metal which is comparatively clean, so allowance has to be made and a larger tip size used when the metal to be cut is covered with rust, scale, or paint. Under such conditions, however, it is often more economical to clean over the line of cut so as to expose clean metal.

Cutting Technique

Assuming that the correct tip size has been selected and that the gas pressures have been adjusted so as to supply the proper volume of oxygen and acetylene, the main point in developing skill is to acquire the habit of advancing the torch at the proper rate. It will be found that after the cut is well started, better progress can be made by slanting the tip of the torch slightly backward. The effect of this is to leave a relatively thin section of metal at the bottom of the cut which is kept well preheated by the combustion process. This makes more rapid work possible, because if the torch tip is held at right angles to the metal the preheating effect must penetrate the full thickness of the section which is being cut. When the end of the cut is reached it is of course necessary to turn the tip so that it is at right angles to the plate in order to complete the cut cleanly.

The skilled operator is able to follow the line of cut accurately and keep up with the rate of preheating so closely that practically no cutting oxygen is wasted. The result of such work is a narrow even kerf and the best operating speed.

High Pressure Is Wasteful

One of the most common faults in cutting is to greatly increase the oxygen pressure with the idea that this will speed up the operation by blowing the molten slag more rapidly out of the kerf. Instead of increasing the speed of the work this usually results in a cooling effect produced by the excess oxygen and an actual slowing up of the work as well as waste of oxygen. The operator will find that a hot gentle preheating flame is more desirable than a bright hissing flame and that the cutting jet is best regulated by starting with the pressure as low as possible and increasing it until it appears to penetrate the full thickness of the metal easily. It should be obvious that when cutting steel the only movement of the torch is directly ahead along the line of cut, there being no motion from side to side as in the case of welding.

A good cut should be comparatively clean and smooth along both faces of the kerf. The top edge should be fairly sharp with no indication of melting done or the edges and the bottom edge will have little or no slag adhering to it. That which does stick to the bottom of the cut should be easily removable with a wire brush.

Hints for Good Cutting

When cutting very thick sections which do not have any sharp corners, the cut can be started more rapidly by using a cold chisel to make a small sharp nick at the point where it is desired to start the cut. When a closed cut is to be made in a piece of sheet metal or plate and it is desired to have the hole as smooth as possible, it is better to drill or cut a hole at an inside point near the line of cut, get the cut started, then carry it to the line and proceed around it. When it is desired to pierce a hole in plate, the surface is first heated to a bright red then the flame is slanted about 45 deg and a rather small supply of cutting oxygen turned on. The flame should be kept slanting until the plate is thoroughly pierced so that the heat and the molten metal will not be forced backward against the torch tip but are always driven away from it. The torch is straightened and the hole reamed

Good and poor kerfs left by cutting.

just as soon as the cut has penetrated the entire section.

Guiding the Line of Cut

Whenever possible, provide some sort of hand rest to assist in guiding the torch smoothly and uniformly. A good heavy straight edge is a big help in straight line cutting. In circle cutting the torch can be mounted in a holder built on the principle of a drawing compass. These mechanical helps will greatly facilitate the work. Where there is a great deal of circle cutting the torch can be mounted in some such device as an old drill press, and the work made to revolve underneath it on a movable gear-operated platform. Sometimes a lathe or planer bed makes a good mounting for a cutting torch for straight line cutting.

Cutting Tanks and Containers

Special attention should be paid to the cutting up of old tanks or containers for scrap. Before starting to make cuts in old tanks for this purpose, it should be determined what liquids or gases they may have contained. If they have carried combustible materials, no cutting of any kind should be started until proper means have been taken to be sure that all traces of combustible liquids or gases have been thoroughly removed from the inside. Heavy steel cylinders which have been used for the transportation and storage of compressed inflammable gases or liquids should not be treated like ordinary scrap. The owner's name should be clearly marked on such containers and when they are found in with scrap material the owner should be notified.

Machine Cutting

As the advantages of welded fabrication have become apparent to manufacturers, substitution of rolled steel shapes and plates for castings has become widespread. The need for an economical method of providing such plates and shapes in the needed patterns has given rise to a new application of oxy-acetylene cutting. Machines have been developed, equipped with specially designed cutting torches, which accurately locate the line of cut, so that practically any design or angle of cut is quickly prepared. An important aspect of machine cutting is that compared with any other method of preparation such as milling or sawing, the flame cut part is more economical. Further advantages from the point of view of the fabricator are that he has an extremely flexible method of fabrication, changes if necessary can be quickly made, stocks of raw materials are kept at a minimum, and pattern costs are eliminated. Many other advantages might be enumerated.

Types in Use

The types of machines on the market are many, ranging from small portable units to permanent installations in sections of the plant set aside for them where materials can be handled with ease and minimum expense. Some are driven with a simple feed screw for straight line cutting. The majority are motor driven with various means of guiding the torch. In some a tracing wheel is used to follow a blue print. Others have a magnetically operated tracing wheel which follows a carefully prepared template of metal. It is generally true that a central control is provided to adjust speed and gas pressures. Many machines can mount two or more torches so that the same part may be cut several times with only one operation.

Advantages of Machine Cutting

The benefits of oxy-acetylene machine cutting are economy of preparation, flexibility of application and elimination of machining costs on finished work. If all these advantages are to be realized there are several important factors to be considered. Manufacturers of this type of equipment have spent a good deal of time and money in perfecting them and assembling data for their correct operation. These recommendations should be followed carefully.

Tip and Speed Selection

With the material at hand, the first consideration is the selection of the proper tip which will be governed by the thickness of the metal. Reference to the chart furnished with the machine will give the correct information. Along with it will be found the pressures for both oxygen and acetylene adjustments and also the speed at which the cut is to be made. The only deviation from this data will be in the case of thin materials and a pattern of intricate shape. The speed of cut may have to be reduced to follow it. In such cases it is at times wise to use a smaller tip with suitable gas pressure and lower cutting speed.

Group the Cutting Jobs

The real economy of machine cutting lies in keeping the machine on actual cutting operations the largest possible part of the work day. This desirable end is accomplished, first by proper selection of tip for the thickness of metal being cut, second by following to the letter the manufacturer's data sheets for gas pressure adjustments and speed of cut. The speed used should be the highest possible consistent with good quality of cut. Another place to watch for cost reduction is in scheduling the materials to be shaped. Where a day's work for the cutting machine can be set up well in advance of requirements, orders should be gone over and thickness of material requisitioned put in groups. In this way time is saved in changing tips and adjusting gas pressures and speed of cut. Study of stock room lay out and cutting machine location will soon suggest ways of feeding materials smoothly and efficiently to the cutting floor. Consideration of methods for removing cut shapes and delivering them to fabricating divisions also offer possibilities for cost reduction.

Stack Cutting

In addition to mounting two or more cutting torches on the guide arm of the machine for the production of duplicate parts, stack cutting offers further possibilities for cost reduction. Several pieces of plate of the same thickness to be cut in the same pattern are securely fastened together. Some method of clamping is the usual means. However, it is sometimes feasible to run a weld bead along several edges so that each sheet is held firmly to the next. Punched holes through which bolts are tightened is a third method. The point to keep in mind is that each sheet should be clamped in close contact as near as possible to the line of cut. The point at which the cut starts should have the edges in close alignment. Stack cutting offers further possibilities of cost reduction in the production of small shapes. There are usually sizable amounts of scrap accumulated. If these are segregated according to thickness, they may be used for stack cutting parts within the limits of their dimensions without drawing new sheets from the stock room.

The desirability of machine cutting lies in the fast production of accurate shapes in sheet, plate and shapes that require little or no fit-up when they reach the assembly floor. Economy of such production centers in low cost per foot of cut in which is involved three factors: cost of gases, labor and overhead. The gas cost for a given thickness of metal remains constant. However, labor and overhead costs go on whether the machine operates or not. Therefore, every short cut that can be used to keep the cutting machine in constant operation is a step in the direction of lower cost per foot of cut. The observing superintendent and operator will soon discover methods of accomplishing this end.

Effect of Flame Cutting

For some time it was considered that the flame cutting process had detrimental effects on the steel cut. It was thought that the metal was oxidized or hardened on the cut surface. Investigations, however, have indicated that steels containing less than 0.35% carbon can be shaped with the oxy-acetylene torch without any damage to the material. In fact, the study indicated that metal so prepared had physical properties which made them superior to like metals prepared by any mechanical means such as shearing, planing, etc. Perhaps the most convincing proof is the fact that the ASME Boiler Code Committee has written into the Power Boiler and Unfired Pressure Vessel Sections acceptance of oxy-acetylene cut materials of less than 0.35% carbon for fabrication into structures coming under those specific code provisions.

Higher carbon and some alloy steels while they can be cut by the oxy-acetylene process, develop certain detrimental characteristics. A thin hardened zone develops on the face of the cut which may be quite brittle and lacks ductility. This undesirable situation can be prevented or corrected by preheating the metal being cut or by subsequent annealing.

Cast Iron Cutting

In demolition work or in foundries it is frequently necessary to reduce large sections of cast iron to small pieces. For some time it was considered that cast iron was almost impossible to cut with the oxy-acetylene cutting torch. The difficulty of cutting this material is probably accounted for by the considerable content of free or graphitic carbon which exists in the metal. However, if the proper technique is followed, cast iron can be successfully cut.

The Tip to Use

From the very nature of the metal, it requires a very high preheat before a line of cut can be carried. A regular cutting torch is required with a tip having more preheating orifices than is required for cutting steel. This provides a flame that will bring the metal to a much higher temperature making it easier to combine the molten metal with oxygen.

Flame Adjustment

The flame adjustment should be distinctly carburizing (excess acetylene) with an acetylene streamer equal, roughly to the thickness of the metal being cut. However, various grades of cast iron will govern this adjustment. Oxygen pressure should not be too high and in general it should be about equal to that required for cutting steel of the same thickness.

Starting the Cut

In starting the cut, the flame should be played along the face of the metal where the cut is to start. When it reaches almost a molten stage at the top surface, the cutting oxygen jet should be opened slowly. Since the oxide has a lower melting point than that of cast iron, the operator should not expect to see the same reaction as when steel is being cut. Some oxidation will occur, but in general in cutting cast iron the stream of oxygen will have a washing effect. With the cut well started the head of the torch should be inclined about 75 deg to the surface with the tip pointing toward the start of the cut.

Torch Manipulation

Unlike steel cutting, cast iron requires a definite movement of the torch. This should be a semi-circular motion across the line of cut extending an equal distance each side of the kerf. Where the section is comparatively thin this side-to-side motion can advance slowly with each half circle, but on heavy sections the advance should be made still more slowly and each half circle should slightly overlap the preceding one. Advancing at too rapid a rate will tend to lose the cut which will be evidenced by the formation of a black spot. This will necessitate going back and reheating the metal as at the start.

Cutting Hints

On extremely thick pieces it may save time if a first cut is made from the face comparatively close

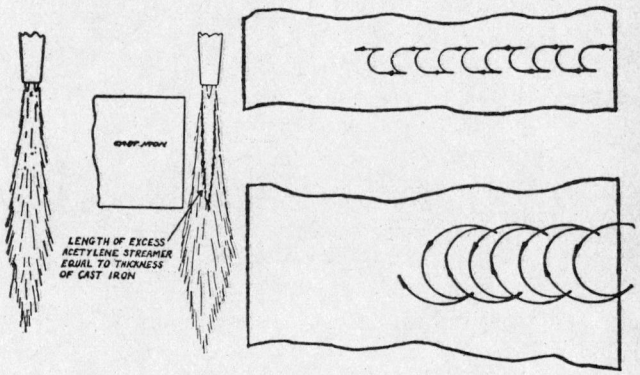

Flame adjustment for cast iron cutting (left) torch manipulation (right).

to the bottom. Another help on heavy material is the oxygen lance which will be described later. Still a further device for carrying on cast iron cutting is to feed in a minimum size steel welding rod as the cut progresses. As the end of the cut is approached the torch head may be inclined almost to an angle of 90 deg and at the far end of the torch should be carried down the far face at about the angle of lag. Thus the cut is completed.

With experience the operator can produce some extremely smooth cuts where they are required. Precaution should be taken in the clothing worn. Hands, arms, eyes, head and legs should be well protected, for some extremely hot molten metal issues from the cut which does not immediately cool as is the case in cutting steel.

The Oxygen Lance

There are many occasions when large masses of metal are to be cut which are beyond the easy range of the cutting torch. Some instances are the scrapping of heavy machinery bases, ingots, piercing holes, etc. A simple, easily applied method of making cuts of this type is made with the oxygen lance. The lance is simply a supply of clean steel pipe, either $\frac{1}{8}$ or $\frac{1}{4}$ in. diameter with connections for oxygen hose, regulators and a supply of oxygen which usually is manifolded because of the quantity needed.

Starting the Cut

The cut is started most easily by heating a point on the metal where the cut is to start with an oxy-acetylene torch until it reaches the kindling temperature. The end of the pipe is brought up and the oxygen turned on. Immediately the same reaction starts as when a cutting torch is used. The main difference is that with the lance there is no preheating flame. However as the cut progresses, the pipe melts and carries the cut along. If an **exceptionally heavy** job is at hand, several lengths of pipe should be available so that as one burns down another can be connected up and the cut completed. It is also well to have two operators working on the job, one to handle the lance and the second to adjust the oxygen pressure which can be comparatively low when the cut starts, but should be increased as the heavy section is reached. Oxygen pressures used usually range from 75 to 100 psi.

Frequently it will be found necessary to use a cutting torch and lance together. In this case the torch carries the cut 3 to 4 in. from the surface where the lance picks it up and carries it to the bottom. Care should be exercised in laying out the work so that as the cut progresses the slag can flow out and away from the section.

Safety Precautions

As in cast iron cutting the operator using an oxygen lance should clothe himself carefully, also being careful to keep out of the way of the piece which is being severed if it is not supported from falling. Frequently ingots are cut after being broken out of the molds and still very hot. The pouring heat which remains is an aid in economical cutting, but it is to the operator's advantage if a shield can be provided which will protect him from the heat.

Flame Cutting Variables

There are really ten important variables that will affect the quality of oxyacetylene cutting. They are:

1. Size of tip oxygen jet.
2. Oxygen speed.
3. Thickness of metal.
4. Cutting speed.
5. Purity of oxygen.

6. Quality of the metal.
7. Intensity of preheat.
8. Angle of cutting oxygen stream to metal.
9. Smoothness of cutting oxygen orifice.
10. Cleanliness of tip end.

Cutting Tip Selection

The importance of the proper size tip for efficient and economical cutting cannot be over-emphasized. All manufacturers of cutting torches have experimented extensively with their torches to determine the tip size best suited for different thickness of metal. These experiments, likewise, have determined the recommended acetylene and oxygen pressures for the individual tip size. This information is furnished in chart form. Cutting tip sizes for various thicknesses of steel are given below.

Cutting Tip Recommendations
(mild steel not preheated)

Thickness of metal inches	Oxygen Jet Drill Size (center hole)	Oxygen pressure, psig (lb per sq in. gauge)	Acetylene pressure, psig (lb per sq in. gauge)
up to 1/8	60	10	3
1/4	60	10-15	3
3/8	55	15-25	3
1/2	55	20-30	4
3/4	55	20-30	4
1	53	25-35	4
1 1/2	53	30-40	4
2	49	40-50	5
3	49	45-55	5
4	49	50-60	5
5	45	50-70	5-6
6	45	60-80	5-6

The operator should develop a technique which will enable him to get satisfactory cutting speed with the recommended tip size and pressures. These recommendations are usually based on the cutting of comparatively clean metal. When cutting metal which is rusty, scaly or has been painted, it is generally suggested that the next larger size recommended tip be used. Often, it is more economical to clean the metal along the line of cut so as to expose clean metal.

Oxy-LP Gas Flame Cutting

Propane (C_3H_8) and Butane (C_4H_{10}) and mixtures thereof were extracted from natural gas and natural gasoline on a crude, experimental basis in West Virginia as early as 1910. By 1922, the extraction of these "wild" members of the petroleum gas family had been increased to only 223,000 gallons (approximately 22 tank carloads) a year. Between 1926 and 1935 improvements in refinery techniques brought forth a new industrial giant, known as "Bottled Gas." This development brought to rural areas beyond the gas mains, new conveniences, which up to then were available only to the city dweller.

By 1953, "bottled gas," compressed gas in portable cylinders, and "tank gas," in larger stationary bulk containers, were serving the domestic needs of over 9 million American homes with "Liquefied Petroleum Gas." It was being used for cooking, refrigeration, water heating, space heating, sterilizing and many rural and agricultural processes. By that time factory equipped propane-powered trucks and farm tractors, first introduced in 1940, had come into common use. These fuels are marketed under countless trade marks, through dealers in nearly every village, but they are commonly known as LP Gas. The most common of the LP Gases is propane.

The general acceptance of LP Gas as a low cost fuel of

many uses, and its complete availability in any area brought it to the attention of the vast welding industry. One cubic foot of propane contains 2520 BTU's of heat as compared with 1475 BTU's per cubic foot of acetylene. This much higher BTU value must not be confused with flame temperature. Because of its chemical structure the maximum flame temperature of oxy-LP Gas is approximately 5300 F and is achieved by using 5 volumes of oxygen (from the cylinder) for each volume of propane burned. Therefore, to produce this maximum flame temperature requires three times as much oxygen to produce the same *volume* of heat, as compared with oxy-acetylene. (3/5 cu ft of propane equals 1 cu ft of acetylene in BTU's).

At this maximum flame temperature of 5300 F, the oxy-propane is 1000 F lower than the oxy-acetylene flame. This makes it entirely unacceptable for fusion welding of iron or steel. The volume of oxygen required to develop a temperature of 5300 F produces a highly oxidizing flame which would burn iron or steel, as explained in Chapter X.

Advantages of Oxy-LP Gas for Flame Cutting

In flame cutting, the function of the preheating flames of the cutting tip, is to raise the temperature of the steel to the critical point (cherry red or approximately 1650 F). At that temperature the steel will burn in an atmosphere of air. Thus, the oxy-LP mixture will do very satisfactorily despite the fact that its flame temperature is lower than oxyacetylene. The starting, or preheating time required to start the cut, will require perhaps two to five seconds longer than with oxyacetylene, depending on whether the start is on the edge of the plate, inside, or piercing the face of the plate. Another factor affecting starting time is the cleanliness of the surface being preheated.

Once the cut has started, the advantages are all in favor of oxy-LP Gas. Because of its gentler, lower temperature flame, the edges of the cut (kerf) are not overheated and a narrower slot (kerf) of metal is burned away. This action requires less cutting oxygen to remove the lesser volume of steel, or conversely will allow the same volume of cutting oxygen to more completely oxidize the metal displaced, depending on the speed at which the torch is advanced. This minimizes the slag adherence to the underside of the kerf which, when present at all, is quite brittle and more easily removed. For the same reason the lower preheat temperature will not melt down the edges of the cut.

Table 1.--Properties of Cutting Fuel Gases

	BTU/CF	Cylinder Pressure (Full) 70	Ignition Temp.	Flame Temp.	Limits of Flammability in Air % Gas in Mixture
Propane C_3H_8	2520	110 psi	1130 F	5300 F	2.3- 9.5
Butane C_4H_{10}	3275	32 psi	1130 F	5300 F	1.9- 8.4
Acetylene C_2H_2	1475	275 psi	896 F	6300 F	3.0-24.0
Hydrogen H_2	325	1800 psi	1076 F	5400 F	4.2-75.0

Only Special Tips Required

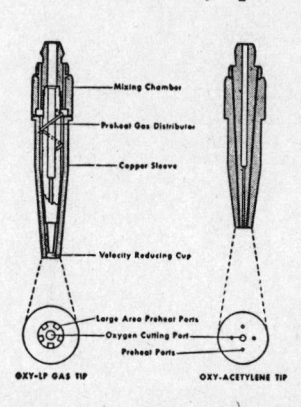

LP Gas is a relatively "slow-burning gas" as compared with acetylene or hydrogen. For this reason special design cutting tips are required. They provide a recess, or cup to retard, or "pilot," and stabilize the flames. In general oxy-LP Gas tips consist of a base for seating the tip in the cutting torch head, into which is inserted a stem, usually of brass, with a central drilled hole for the cutting oxygen and with milled slots on the outer surface of the stem for the preheat orifices. Over this stem is provided a swaged copper "external" or barrel or sleeve. which being about 3/16 to 1/4 in. longer than the stem. results in a recess or cup being formed on the outer end when assembled. The preheating gases "rub" against the inner wall of the sleeve which pilots and stabilizes the combustion.

This special tip is the only addition required to use LP Gas with the standard flame cutting outfit. The torch. regulators and hose are the same as for oxy-acetylene flame cutting.

Back firing, pre-ignition and flash back which have been common with "fast-burning" acetylene under abusive conditions of operation, are practically impossible to produce with LP Gas because of its slow-burning nature. When tips become fouled with slag this can be easily removed by cooling the tip and disassembling the external sleeve.

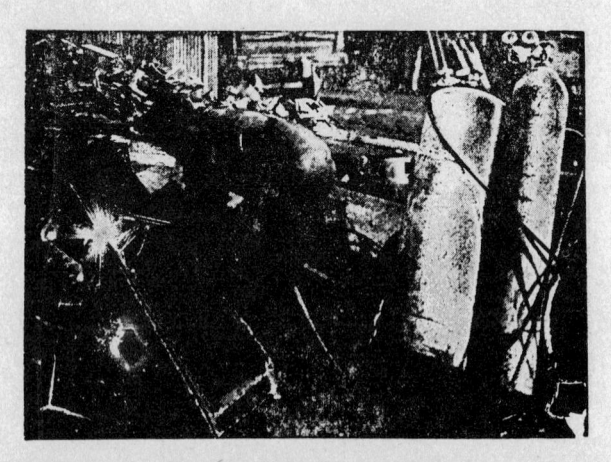

Much of the flame cutting of scrap steel is done with oxy propane cutting equipment.

Three Rules for Efficient Flame Adjustment

Maximum efficiency requires exact adjustment of the proportion of preheating oxygen to LP Gas volume. As stated before, five volumes of oxygen are required to one volume of LP Gas in the preheating flames. Fortunately, there are three methods to definitely determine this ratio.

(1) Minimum Cone Length: Open fuel gas needle valve and ignite gas, pressing tip lightly at 45 deg. angle against fire brick or metal. Turn on oxygen preheat valve and inner cones will snap back so that combustion starts in the recessed cup. Lift torch head, gradually increase oxygen volume, and inner cones will become progressively shorter as oxygen supply is increased, until the flames become shortest *and* then begin to elongate. *The proper adjustment is the shortest length of cone.*

(2) Water Bucket Test: Fill a pail with water to within four inches of the top. Light and adjust torch as described above. Gently immerse tip into the water to a depth of say, two inches. The flame will burn under water. If insufficient oxygen is being supplied those gases which have not been combusted will burn with air on the surface of the water. Slowly increase oxygen adjustment *just until burning of the gases above the water ceases. This is the proper adjustment.*

(3) Black Spots on Preheated Surface: Adjust preheat as described above. Apply preheat to clean surface of steel. (Not on the edge.) Hold tip so that ends of inner cones of flames just touch the surface and as temperature rises, a bright cherry spot will glow on the steel under each preheat cone. If insufficient oxygen is supplied a small black spot will appear in the center of each bright spot. *Slowly increase the oxygen adjustment until the black spots vanish. This is the proper adjustment.*

The three methods cited are exact, simple to master, and

triple-check each other. As the operator gains experience he will quickly adapt one of those methods to his liking, but can always reasure himself by cross-checking with the others, thus having confidence in the efficiency of his flame cutting operation.

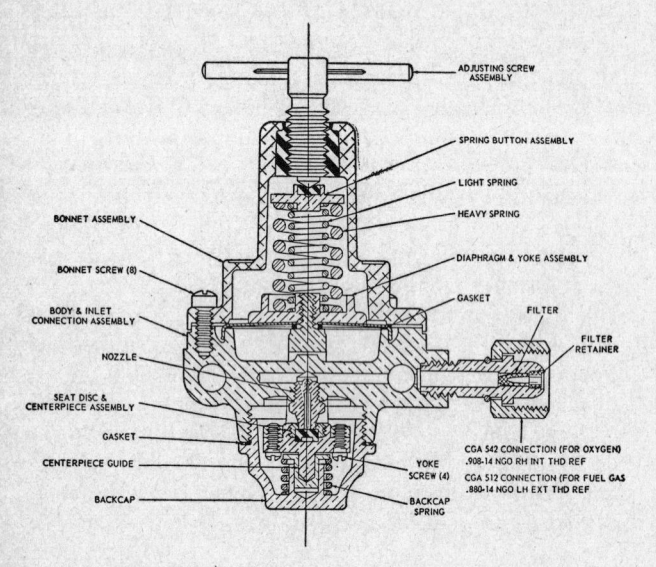

Bolted and flange bonnet type pressure reducing regulator. Note various internal parts. See also pages 27 and 29.

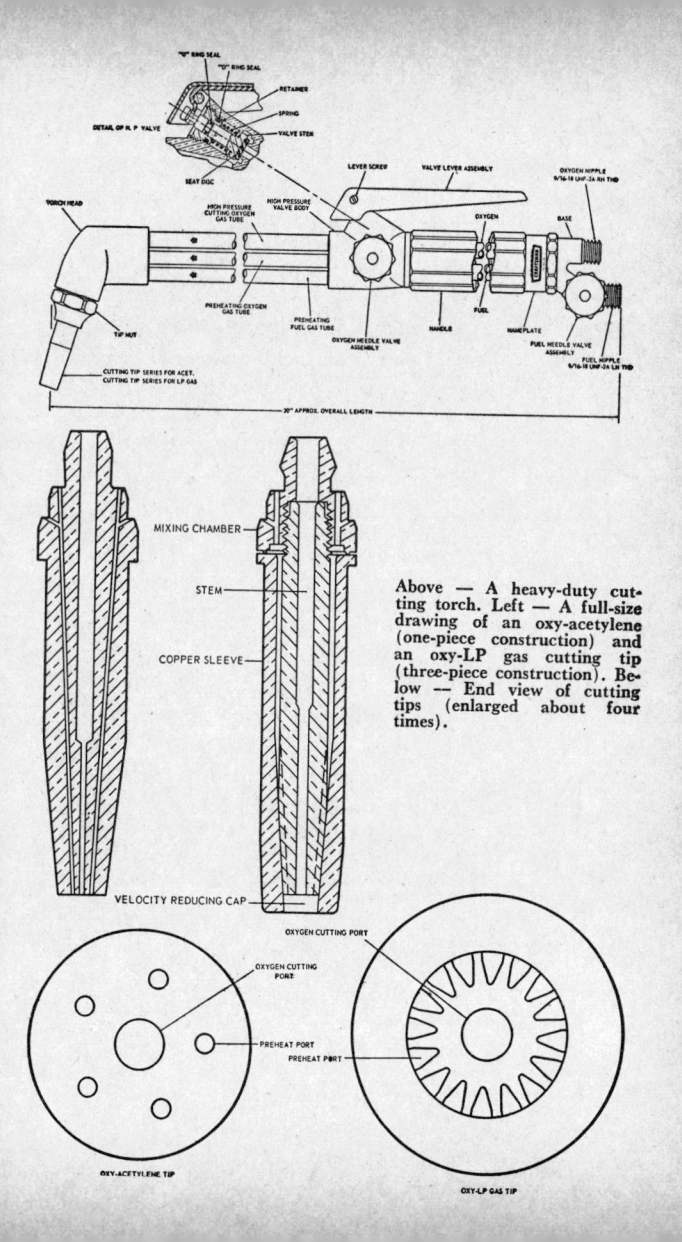

Above — A heavy-duty cutting torch. Left — A full-size drawing of an oxy-acetylene (one-piece construction) and an oxy-LP gas cutting tip (three-piece construction). Below — End view of cutting tips (enlarged about four times).

CHAPTER 13
WELDING FOR FUN

The number of home craftsmen working with metal is increasing constantly. For years the home craftsman was a wood-worker. This is being changed with the increasing use of metal furniture, and the fact that the home craftsman now has welding and cutting equipment with which to work. Most hobbyists realize that metal-working tools which will perform functions similar to those of woodworking tools are quite expensive. Also, the average person feels that a hobby involving metal-working is beyond his ability. But the home craftsman with a welding outfit, knows this is not the case.

Not only does the gas welding and cutting outfit provide the home craftsman with a quick and efficient means of joining and severing metals, it also provides a fast-working process for heating, straightening, hardening, softening, and cleaning metals. In addition, for those whose hobby takes them into ceramics or enamel copper jewelry making, the welding torch may easily replace the kiln.

Things to Do

The skilled home weldor may readily become the neighborhood repairman if not careful. As his skills become known, his garage becomes filled with broken lawnmowers, tricycles, and other gadgets friends want fixed. His greatest pleasures, however, will probably come from those activities devoted to the fabrication of wrought iron items for the home. While this chapter will point out a few of the items that can be made with the aid of a welding torch, the

WELDING FOR FUN

possibilities are unlimited. The only restriction is a lack of imagination. The welding torch may be used to produce coffee tables, clothes racks, lamps, bookracks, pictures, or even sculptured works. Hobby welding is not confined to the indoors, it can go outdoors for barbeque grills, porch railings, or even a patio canopy.

As the craftsman begins to work in mental with a torch, he gets a whole new concept of design and fabrication. He can do things that are impossible to attain in wood. In welding he can correct slight mistakes that would be ruinous in a wood-working project. By its very nature, welding helps him produce professional results.

Hobby welding is relaxing; the home weldor may set his own pace. His activities take him into a program as elaborate, or as simple as he wishes.

Materials to Use

The craftsman weldor is sometimes confronted with a material problem, but here again, ingenuity comes into play. Various size welding rods are extremely useful. Startling effects can be obtained by using steel rods which are painted black, together with polished bronze rods to produce black and gold combinations. For large size rods the solid curtain rods at the hardware store solve the problem. Conduit in various diameters can be obtained from electrical supply houses. Sheet-metal shops have perforated metal. Plumbing shops, weldable pipe; and the local job welding shop will carry a stock of small angles, channels, flats, squares and rounds. Probably the most interesting place of all, particularly when a special project is in mind, will be the local junk yard.

Bricktop Welding Table

The first job for the home weldor should be a good solid welding table, having a fire brick top, and steel angle legs.

262 OXY-ACETYLENE WELDER'S HANDBOOK

The size of the table is not too important, though it probably should not be less than 17 in. square. A rectangular table 17 in. x 30 in. is more desirable and one fitted with a swivel vise on one corner will be found extremely helpful.

Cylinder Truck

The cylinder truck to make an oxy-acetylene welding and cutting unit portable, is a desirable addition to any shop, and probably the second best project that can enter into a

from:
1 pc–¾ in. pipe 42 in. long
1 pc–16 ga sheet 12 in. x 15 in.
1 pc–16 ga sheet 6 in. square (cut diagonally for gusset)
1 pc–¼ in. x 1 in. bar 2 ft. long
2 pc–1¼ x 1¼ x ⅛ in. angle 3 in. long
1 pc–Rd bar stock for axle to suit
1 pc–Chain 36 in. long
 ¼ in. welding rod for spark lighter and chain loops

Fig. 1—A single handle cylinder truck of welded construction can be fabricated

Fig. 2—Four scrap pieces of pipe will make a handy scroll and circle former.

newly found career as a hobby weldor. The single handle truck, Fig. 1, is capable of hauling all but the largest cylinders and will usually prove adequate for the home craftsman. Probably the most difficult part of this project is the forming of the $1/16$ in. steel sheet used for a platform. Short angles behind and a triangular gusset provide reinforcement. If this piece is obtainable from a sheet metal shop, it would probably be best to have them "break" it to obtain the desired shape. The $1\frac{1}{2}$ x 6 in. rubber tired wheels can probably be obtained from the local hardware store. The axle size, which should not be less than $\frac{1}{2}$ in. diameter, may be larger depending upon the requirements of the wheel hubs. Flame heating is desirable to ease the problem of bending the pipe handle. With the welding table and cylinder truck at hand, the hobby weldor will have the working conditions available to make him better able to duplicate the work of the skilled craftsman.

If hobby welding plans include metal furniture and lamps, another item that will be found of considerable value, is a jig for producing uniform bends of various sizes, in $\frac{1}{4}$ in. or smaller diameter rods.

Such a jig is made of short lengths of scrap pipe, using a small piece of angle which has been welded to the pipe for a hold-down feature. A rod bending jig which will permit the production of uniform graceful bends, and not only will it save time, but add to the beauty of the welding projects undertaken.

Wrought Iron Items

What to build first is always a problem for the newly discovered metal craftsman. Anything undertaken will help improve welding skill. It's generally recommended, however, that the more difficult task be left until such times as handling of the welding torch has become quite skillful.

On initial projects, even the more simple items attempted

may end up crude in appearance. Don't get discouraged! Generally little is lost should the project be discarded completely and started over.

Magazine Racks

The average home has many uses for magazine racks. The home weldor with ingenuity can build a variety of

Fig. 3—A black and gold magazine rack with each rod on the basket hooking into place.

Fig. 4—This rack has a removable basket and the important handle for carrying.

racks, so that each of the bedrooms, the recreation room, as well as the living room and den have magazine racks. No two have to be alike. A magazine rack is an excellent beginning project. The material involved is readily at hand, inasmuch as welding rod may be used in building the framework as well as the magazine holding basket.

One quarter inch diameter welding rod is generally used for the structural frame of a magazine rack. The basket is generally fabricated from $1/8$ in. welding rod. When steel rods are used on these projects, the finished piece is usually painted a dull black. However, variety may be obtained by using bronze rods on the basket to produce a black and gold magazine rack. One of the simpler racks of this design is shown in Fig. 3.

Dimensions are not too important in a magazine rack. Each rack should be long enough to take the largest size magazine, which means an overall length of at least 16 in. The height of the rack should be sufficient to accommodate a magazine 10 in. wide and still allow the basket to clear the floor by $1\frac{1}{2}$ to 2 inches. Other than meeting these general dimensional requirements, the design of the rack rests entirely in the ingenuity of the home craftsman.

The rack frame in Fig. 3, is formed from $\frac{1}{4}$ in. welding rod. The open inverted "U"s which form the legs, were made by bending straight pieces of rod over the jig shown in Fig. 2. To these pieces are welded two side members which were formed by bending a 32 in. length of welding rod at right angles 8 in. from each end. A 36 in. length of rod was bent in a huge arc to provide the handle. These pieces were all braze welded to form the basic frame.

The basket was fabricated using 6 — 36 in. x $\frac{1}{8}$ in. bronze rods. Each end of the rod was bent to form a hook, then the rods were placed on the welding table spaced 3 in. apart, with the hooks up. They were then tied together by bronze welding a $\frac{1}{8}$ in. rod across the center of each of the six, with another $\frac{1}{8}$ in. rod welded across them at a point 5 in. from each end. The entire basket frame then is bent into a "U" and hooked over the basic frame to form a pleasing, colorful magazine rack.

The rack in Fig. 4, is also a black and gold type, but presents a somewhat more difficult welding problem, inasmuch as 12 bronze rods are used in the baskets. The ends of these rods are brazed to a $\frac{1}{4}$ in. weld rod, so as to make this an all welded affair. The support rods of the basket merely drop over the hooks which tie the side members together. The handle, in this instance, forms the center member and is brazed to the curved pieces on the ends of the rack.

A handle is desirable for all magazine racks, as it provides a ready means of moving the rack from one place to another. Always consider this in a design.

Fig. 5 pictures two all steel magazine racks and shows possible variety in their construction. The small rack on the left, Fig. 5, is fabricated from $1/4$ in. steel rod for the basic frame, with $1/8$ in. steel rod forming the basket portion. This rack is designed so that the sides may be loaded separately, since they are separated by a U-shaped piece formed from a $1/8$ in. rod which is welded to the central frame to form a handle.

An all steel magazine rack may be either welded or

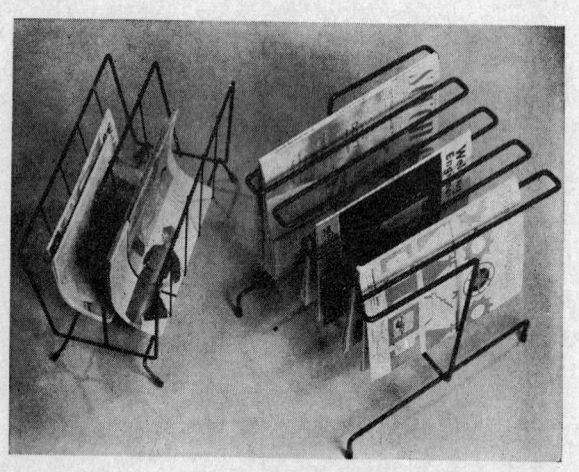

Fig. 5—All steel magazine racks are usually painted black.

brazed as the home craftsman desires. Generally speaking most home weldors obtain more desirable results from brazing. It is done at a lower temperature and gives better control of working conditions.

The magazine rack on the right, Fig. 5, was formed from $5/16$ in. rod. In this instance 14 ft. of rod was used. After a careful layout had been worked out on paper, the rod was heated at the proper spots and bent at right angles to form a uniform series of elongated U's. The ends of the rods were bent at 90 deg. to the plane of the other bends, and again bent at 90 deg. to meet and were joined by welding. This framework was then welded to two pieces of $5/16$ in. rod, which formed the support and feet of this stand.

As seen from these four examples, the only factor that limits design in magazine racks, is the lack of imagination.

Fig. 6—Heavier rods are used for the brass plated vanity bench (left). The basic design of the bookshelf (right) serves many purposes.

Book Cases and Racks

Another popular wrought steel item for the home are holders of books—book shelves and book racks. These racks become end tables, telephone stands, planters, or a variety of "holders" of miscellaneous items. Here again, ¼ in. welding rods play an important role in building the basic structure frame while the shelving is usually made up of ⅛ in. welding rod. The shelves are very similar to those found in most ovens. Should the home weldor have any trouble it might be well to examine an oven shelf to see where the fault may lie. Sometimes 3/16 in. diameter rods are used for the end members and center separators.

The simplest type of book shelf is that shown in Fig. 6 (right). Dimensions of shelves vary to suit conditions at hand. If building a shelf or table for a particular spot, it should be of such a size as to fill the bill. Usually, however, these smaller shelves are designed to end table size, about 12 in. wide and 26 to 30 in. long. Usually the shelf is not more than 2½ times as long as it is wide. Spacing of the shelves may vary; 8 to 10 in. represents good spacing, with the lower shelf about 4 in. off the floor.

By using the same basic design of Fig. 6, right, but by bending the two upper shelves at right angles, it's possible to obtain the magazine rack and bookshelves seen in Fig. 7.

Fig. 8 represents another type of book shelf, and its construction is trickier in that the shelves are made then the bottom two are threaded on to the legs before the cross members are welded in place. The shelves are then tack welded to the cross members and also tied to each other by ⅛ in. vertical welding rods at the corners. While these corner rods serve no structural purpose, they do prevent injuries that might result from bumping into the sharp corners of the shelves.

By going into a heavier rod, ⅜ and ½ in. diam., it's possible to fabricate a very sturdy bench such as the one pictured in Fig. 6, left. Such a bench might be used in any room in the house, and is ideally suited for a vanity bench. The seat area is made of expanded metal brazed to the frame. After this job was completed, the entire bench was

WELDING FOR FUN 269

Fig. 7—Angle shelves really hold the books in place.

Fig. 8—Wrought iron shelves serve a variety of uses.

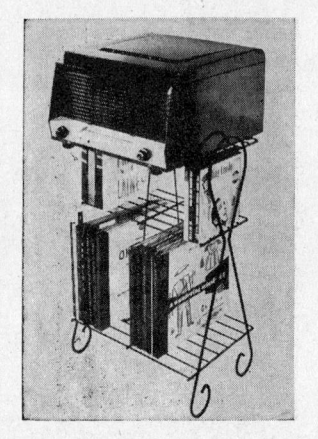

Fig. 9—The bookshelf of Fig. 6 is modified to make a record player stand.

Fig. 10—A welded telephone stand with shelves for the phone books.

brass plated, so as to present a more pleasing appearance.

The record player, Fig. 9, is a shortened version with a few modifications of the table in Fig. 6. It is lower so as to place the record player at the right level, and the shelf spacing has been varied to accommodate various size albums. The home weldor is in the fortunate position of being able to "tailor" various types of stands to meet whatever conditions demand.

Telephone Stand

Another example of a specially designed stand is the telephone stand, Fig. 10. Here again ¼ in. welding rod was used for the basic frame with shelves being fabricated from ⅛ in. rod. Note that the top shelf has unusually close spacing to provide a better working area.

Not all of the things the home weldor fabricates from welding rod are extremely bulky. For example the items pictured in Fig. 11, are simple to construct and serve useful purposes, though small in size. In the lower left of Fig. 11, is pictured a card holder, which is fabricated from perforated metal and a piece of ¼ in. welding rod that was formed into a 5 in. diameter ring and cut in two. In somewhat larger sizes, the same design could be used for a book rack.

In the upper left and right side of Fig. 11, are two examples of ceramic trivets. One in the upper left is formed from ⅛ in. welding rod which has been welded to a 20 gage steel pan so as to form handles and legs for the pan. After the welding job was completed, the pan which had been fabricated to the proper size for holding 56 small ceramic tiles, was filled with these tiles to finish the job. The trivet on the right, which was fabricated from ⅛ in. rod also, is larger in design and holds a 9 in. square ceramic tile.

Figs. 12 and 13, picture two simple book racks which

WELDING FOR FUN

Fig. 11—Small items about the home may be welded, too.

have been fabricated from ¼ in. welding rod. They represent simple but useful objects for any home craftsman.

Wrought Iron Furniture

While most of the items described have been in the home accessory group, there's no reason why the hobby weldor

Fig. 12—A simple book rack from ¼ in. welding rod.

Fig 13—Scrolls dress-up this "welding rod" book rack.

cannot fabricate his own decorative wrought iron furniture. This type of furniture is becoming increasingly popular with today's value conscious home owners. Furniture stores everywhere display wrought iron coffee tables, and examples of attractive four piece luncheon sets and other attractive wrought iron examples that can be made in a few hours from in-expensive mild steel stock. On these larger projects, the hobby weldor will have the opportunity of testing his skill at heating, forming, welding and cutting to quickly transform a few pieces of steel into a piece for the home or terrace.

The first step in building a luncheon set for example, is that of measuring the steel and cutting it to size. The hobby weldor can check store models for measurement, or work to his own measurement to meet special requirements. After determining the measurements for each part, use chalk, soapstone or a punch mark to indicate the line of cut. Flame cutting should be done with a steady hand to insure a smooth straight cut every time.

The various parts may be joined either by fusion welding, or by braze welds. Generally, braze welding is preferred because it is the easiest and fastest way to make the strong joints, in this type of furniture, that will assure a life time of sturdiness for each piece. It must be remembered that the success of braze welding depends not upon one, but a combination of favorable conditions. These conditions can be obtained only by adhering only to proper braze welding techniques as is outlined in the Jiffy Welding Guides.

You'll get clean, strong joints every time if you remember to follow these important steps:

A. Thoroughly clean the weld area.
B. Avoid melting the steel in preheating, just heat to a dull red.
C. Move the flame and the puddle slowly around the

weld area. If the puddle bubbles the work is too hot—draw the flame back for a few seconds.

D. Dip the rod into the brazing flux often.

Decorative scrolls can be used to put finishing touches to each piece of furniture. Such scrolls can be bent into shape using the jig pictured in Fig. 2. A coat of paint, chair cushions and a glass table top complete the set—a truly functional addition to the home that will always be in style.

Small Tables

The ceramic top hall table takes us away from the lighter bar stock and welding rod construction methods into the heavier materials. This table, which had a pan formed from 16 gage material, was fabricated primarily from 1 in. x ¼

Fig. 14—Flat bars are used in the frame of a tile top table.

in. bar stock. The legs were merely inverted U's welded to a bent piece of bent stock which formed the feet. The pan was tack welded to the upper end of the legs, while 1/8 in. welding rods were welded to spacers midway between. These rods serve no structural purposes, and could be omitted if desired. After the welding job was completed, a decorative design was worked out in ceramic tile.

CHAPTER 14

THE SCULPTOR WELDOR

Weldors are turning to art, and artist and sculptors are turning to welding. Both have found that welding is an easy quickly learned technique that can be readily adapted to sculpturing. Because of this ease of adaptation, the artist or sculptor is at an advantage in welded sculpturing. He has the background training and experience in aesthetics and composition that can quickly be used to advantage in welded sculpture.

Welded sculpture is becoming increasingly popular, and it is now estimated that there are nearly as many would-be sculptors as there are weldors in the U.S. Some of these artisans are doing outstanding work, while the most accurate word to describe the efforts of others is "atrocious".

Actually, the use of welding in modern sculpture has developed gradually, although it is the first new technique employed in this art form in over 2,000 years. It was not until the 1930's that the first significant changes in the traditional means of expression in metal sculpture took place. (Until this recent period, the three dimensional form in metal was produced only by the ancient method of casting).

Then, a third of the way into this century, two very distinct movements with strongly opposing philosophies emerged to generate new ideas which would liberate sculpture from the limitations of the foundry. One of these was the constructiveness group, who chose as their medium materials of modern industry. The other, the surrealists, made the biggest impact at the time because of their delvings into the subconscious.

Today, sculptors of every artistic philosophy are utilizing the welding processes in their works. While oxyacetylene welding plays an important part in this activity, sculpturing is not limited to this process. Arc welding finds widespread use, particularly in the joining of such dfficult-to-weld metals as aluminum and stainless steel.

Artistic Ability

There is always the question of how much artistic ability or temperament is required for a weldor to become a sculptor. There seems to be little doubt that to become a true artist, you will need art training. To sell (if that is what you're interested in doing), however, seemingly requires only the ability to join metals. If what you join together holds together, you may well find someone who will want to purchase it.

One of the requirements for welding sculpture is imagination. You also must have the right materials, and some ability as a weldor. In welded sculpture, as in so many other activities, it is always best to start small and work up to the bigger things. By starting on a small-scale project, the object will be easy to work with, will fit the limitations of your work area and your pocketbook, and will not consume so much time as to become a real drag.

The weldor, however, can develop artistic skills, and assisted by a vivid imagination, produce welded sculptures of the most pleasing variety. All have seen the use of welding merely to join together bits and pieces that may have been cut from metal or found in a junk pile. While this nut and bolt, gear and pipe type of sculpture sometimes produces "cute" or unusual effects, there is a great deal of sameness in "constructions" made of these materials. (The term "constructions" is used here because all too few of these endeavors merit the classification of "sculpture"!) The artistic weldor or sculptor should use his imagination to develop an individual expression rather than to copy stereotype applications of welded art. Copying may be employed, however, to develop skill in the welding techniques.

Now that you have mastered some of the techniques and skills of oxy-acetylene welding, you may be ready to try your hand at welded sculpture. Before undertaking this, however, it will be necessary for you to gather together some materials and, possibly, some additional tools.

For your initial efforts in this new hobby, don't undertake a project so long that it cannot be finished in one session. This should not be a long and tiring session either, since such tedious activities tend to be discouraging.

The basic equipment, of course, will be an oxyacetylene outfit, as well as the regular welding tools, such as a wire brush, chipping hammer, several sizes of "C" clamps, several sizes of pliers, and a ballpeen hammer. Other tools that will come in handy as you proceed with your sculpturing activities include locking-plier type wrenches, of both the conventional type and the split jaw type. A duckbill snips, or compound leverage snips, that is capable of cutting left, right and straight ahead, and a good capacity bolt cutter will also be found to be handy supplements to your usual tools.

In the way of materials, there should be a variety of bronze welding rods ranging from $\frac{1}{16}$ to $\frac{1}{4}$ in. in diameter, and mild steel rods in the same size range. A silver brazing alloy should also be obtained, together with a good silver brazing flux. Of course, the brazing rods also will require a flux.

As to the materials to be welded, this will depend a great deal upon the sculpturing planned. In many instances, the variety of welding rods available will serve as sculpturing material. Many projects will involve the use of $1/16$ in. steel sheet. Thin gauge copper and brass sheets will also prove handy. These can be obtained from a local supplier, found in your Yellow Pages under "Metal Products" or a specific heading.

WELDING METAL FLOWERS

A variety of flower forms can be reproduced in metal through welding. While they are not much of a demonstration of artistic ability, they do have a pleasing appearance yet do not require advanced welding techniques. One of the easiest and most delicate is the welded rose.

The Welded Rose

For this project you will need some sheets of 0.010-inch thick cold-rolled steel, 0.010-inch copper and 0.010-inch brass. This material can be obtained from a metal warehouse and you should probably buy the pieces about three feet square, although they may have some scrap strips that will serve your purpose.

Out of each of these sheets should be cut two or three pieces about 3 inches square. To make the yellow rose, take two of the brass squares (one of which will be the "outside" of the flower), a copper square and a steel square, and using a nail, punch a hole in the center of each. (For a red rose, use a couple of copper sheets and one of brass, again punching a hole in the center of each.)

Now, outline four petals on each of the metal squares, in the shape of a four-leaf clover. (See Fig. 1). Using

OXY-ACETYLENE WELDOR'S HANDBOOK 279

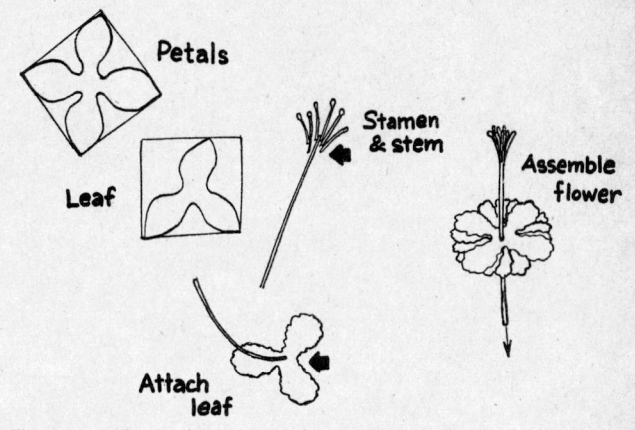

Fig. 1—Steps in creating the welded rose begin with cutting out the petal and leaf shapes, being somewhat free in the design to more accurately duplicate nature.

Figs. 2, 3—Variations of welded flowers challenge the more ambitious weldor.

280 THE SCULPTOR WELDOR

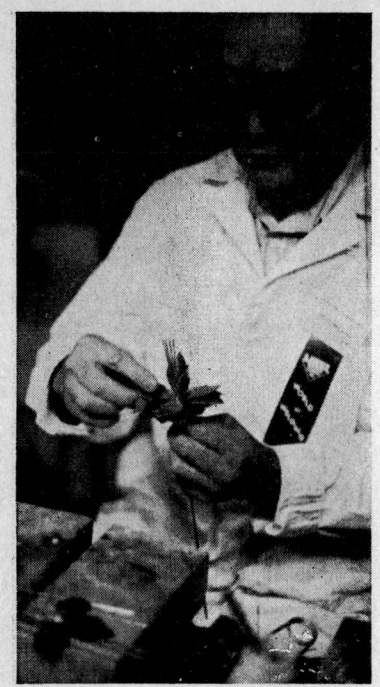

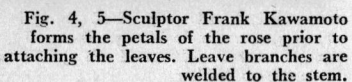

Fig. 4, 5—Sculptor Frank Kawamoto forms the petals of the rose prior to attaching the leaves. Leave branches are welded to the stem.

Fig. 5—The completed rose grouped on a rock with pussy willows.

your smallest welding torch tip, melt away the metal along the outline, so as to develop four connected petals on each plate. Exercise care so as not to burn into the punched hole in the center. Don't worry about the raggedness of the edge or the fact that there are globules of metal left along them. When you have completed "cutting" the four plates, you will have sixteen petals for your initial rose.

The stem

Now let's make a stem for the rose. This is done by taking the wire cutter and clipping off a piece of $3/32$ bronze welding rod about nine or ten inches long. Again with the wire cutters, clip off six or seven pieces of $1/16$ inch bronze rod about three inches long. Now dipping the shorter rods into the flux, braze them individually to the end of the longer rod, so as to form a stem with seven or eight stamen. This cluster of small rods should be melted off so that they are 1 in. to $1\frac{1}{2}$ in. long. In this melting process, there will be a small globule formed on the end of each stamen, which adds to the authenticity of this metal flower.

Having completed the stem and the petals, they are now ready to be assembled. This is simply a matter of slipping the petals onto the stem. To make a yellow rose, a brass sheet with its four petals is first slipped on to the stem. This is followed by a steel sheet, then a copper sheet, and lastly, a second brass sheet.

The various sheets should be rotated so that the petals do not lie on top of one another. Then, holding the stem in an inverted position so that the sheets are more or less tight against the base of the stamens, the stem rod is painted with a silver brazing flux in the area of the petal sheets, after which the sheets are brazed in place with a silver alloy.

The rose bloom is now formed by bending the petals

upward and the edges inward, to form cups around the stamen.

The leaves

If only a single rose is desired, the next move is now to make the leaves. If the project involves a bunch of roses, then additional roses are made and they are attached to a common stem. This attachment is done by silver brazing.

To make the leaves for the roses, the 3 in. x 3 in. sheets are again used. In this instance, however, instead of outlining four petals, only three petals are made (a 3-leaf clover). Again, the surplus metal is melted away, using a small tip welding flame. After melting out the number of leaves you feel that are necessary for the rose, leaf stems are then made by cutting pieces of $1/16$ inch welding rod about 5 inches long. One end of the rod is brazed to the leaf. This brazing is done on what becomes the underside of the leaf, so as to form a three leaf cluster on each stem. Each leaf is grooved through the center and shaped in an irregular fashion so as to give variety to the leaf. The leaf stem is now curved and silver-brazed to the main stem of the rose. Three or four such leaves are brazed at various locations along the stem so as to produce the finished rose.

The Welded Tulip

If you enjoy making metal flowers, a tulip can be made in a fashion very similar to that used in constructing the rose. Instead of using a square sheet for the petal, a rectangular sheet about $1\frac{1}{2}$ inch by 5 inches long is needed. Here again, a nail hole is made in the center of the sheet for subsequent threading on to the stem. Two tulip petals are made at a time, and their shape is more oval than pointed, as in the case of the rose petals. The tulip stem with its stamen is made in the same manner as the stem of the rose.

Again, the petals are slipped on the stem, care being taken to see that the petals overlap so that there are no openings in the flower. To do the job it requires four sheets, making eight petals. After having been silver brazed in place, they are again shaped into a cup form.

The leaves

Tulip leaves are cut from sheets similar to those used for the petals, without the punched hole however. They should be cut into a canoe-shape (when viewed from the top) using tin snips. After this, the small welding torch flame is used for melting the edge. A leaf is formed by bending it lengthwise, from point to point, along the edge of a table or a board. One end is then silver-soldered to the tulip stem, and formed into a natural shape. (Some should be bent "dog-eared," to duplicate nature.)

On tulips, all of the leaves rise from a single junction on the main stem rather than being distributed along the stem as in the case of a rose. Usually two to three leaves are used to complete the tulip.

Metallic Pussywillows

Another free-standing and easily made decorative piece that might be displayed in arrangement with tulips, roses and similar flowers, is the pussywillow branch. Its main stem should be made from a $1/8''$ bronze welding rod, 16 to 20-inches in length. Pussywillow buds are made by merely welding drops of bronze at irregular intervals along the main stem. These drops should be made so that they are teardrop in shape, with the rounded end pointing upward. You'll be able to do this easily by holding the branch upside down while the welding is done.

Welded pussywillows should be made as they are found in nature, either as a single branch or a main branch with shoots. If the latter is used, the shoots and the main branch are made from the same size welding rod. The buds will extend to the top of the branch, but should not be on the bottom four to six inches of the stem.

Free standing pussywillow stems and branches may be placed in vases or bases made of wood, stone, plaster of paris, etc.

Welded Cattails

Cattails can be welded art objects, but usually these are mounted on plaques for wall hanging, rather than permitted to stand free. In such arrangement three to five cattails are usually clustered to appear to be arising from a common stem which is hidden by the leaves at the base of the cluster.

Depending upon the size of the wall plaque to be made, the stems of the cattail can be from one ft to two ft in length. The size of the welding rod used for such a construction and the length and diameter of the cattail depends upon the overall length of the stems.

The body of a cattail is formed from a rectangular 0.010" brass sheet, similar to that used in the making of a tulip. To form the body of the cattail, the sheet should be rolled over a dowel or other round form so as to obtain a uniformly round section, approximately five times the diameter of the welding rod to be used for the stem. The seam of the body is then silver brazed together to form an unbroken cylinder.

Following this, the stem is slipped through this cylindrical body and permitted to protrude out the other end. This extension should vary from cattail to cattail, but probably should be no more than one-half the length of the body of the cattail. The total length of the stem should be at least five times the length of the cattail.

Once the stem has been inserted into the cattail, the ends of the cattail body cylinder are carefully folded in until they fit snugly around the stem. The cattail body is now ready to be brazed into place.

This process is repeated until the desired number of cattails stems have been made. Care should be exercised not to place all of the bodies the same distance from the end, nor should the bodies all have a uniform length. Now that several cattails have been fabricated they should be welded together at the bottom to form a cluster. This cluster area is now covered with leaves, usually two sets on each side of the stem.

Cattail leaves

Cattail leaves are very similar to tulip leaves — formed in the same manner, except that they are from two to three times as long. After being grooved, they are brazed to the cluster then shaped as desired. The cattail piece is now ready to be mounted on a plaque.

Embellishments

As the weldor-sculptor becomes more proficient and adventurous, he may wish to try constructing "spiderwebs" between the cattails, brazing small diameter bronze wire into a web design. For added authenticity, a bronze "glob" spider, complete with eight legs, could be affixed somewhere on such a web!

ADDITIONAL PROJECTS

Some who are working with welding sculpture would rather use the materials at hand than to go out and obtain a variety of materials to do work in this field. The most available material is, of course, the bronze or steel welding rod that is used for joining purposes. These welding rods, in various sizes, can be used for making a variety of objects, ranging from wall hangings to freestanding welded sculpture.

In the area of free-standing, among the common objects to be formed by welding rods or wires together is a baby carriage or an antique automobile, such as the one pictured on page 288. For you to undertake a similar project, all you actually need is your welding outfit; however, you'll find the job easier if you also have a good wire-cutting pliers at hand.

THE FISH PLAQUE

Before starting the fabrication of a fish, you should sketch it out full size on a sheet of paper. Your fish doesn't have to look like any other known fish — just close enough so that others don't have to ask what it is. The sketch, however, should show the location of fins, tail fins, gills, eyes, etc. Pieces of wire or welding rod should be cut to length to conform with the outlines of the sketch. Generally, for a wall hanging of this type, a steel welding rod is used, since the sculptor will probably want to paint it. For contrast, the eye and gill outlines may be made from bronze rods, which could be polished to provide variety in the finished object.

Since the rods involved in the making of a fish wall hanging are probably of a 3/16" or 1/8" diameter, these can usually be formed by hand to obtain the desired curved flowing outline. To make the curves in the shorter pieces, it may be necessary to bend them to shape over a piece of pipe, bar stock or some other round material.

For one who is going to become a sculptor, it's a good idea to become somewhat of a junk collector, too. If you get into this practice, you should soon be able to collect a variety of short lengths of pipe, of various diameters ranging from 1/2" diameter to about 2" in diameter, in 1/4" increments. By gripping a couple of pieces in a vise and using them as a mandrel, it's possible to make a variety of different size rings, smooth graceful curves, etc. When working with shorter lengths of rod and heavier thicknesses, it will be found advisable to grip one end in a plier-type vise while using a ballpeen hammer to bend the rod over a pipe mandrel.

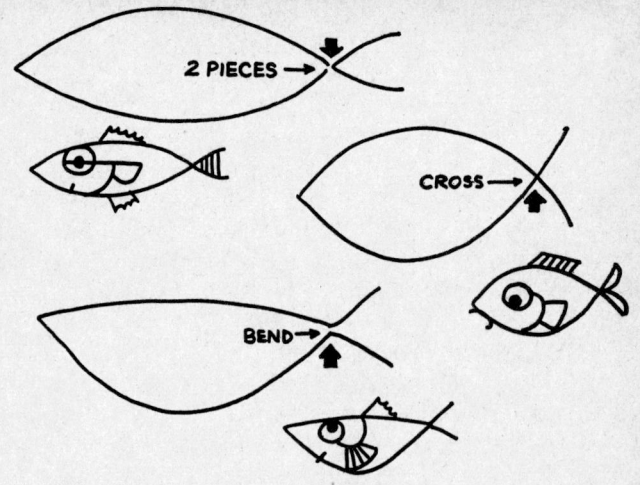

Fig. 7—Some of the methods of forming the outline of welded fish, plus how they could be finished.

If the fish being made is only to be 10" or 12" long, one weld can be eliminated by taking a 36" length of welding rod, bending it in half and doubling it back on itself so as to form both the upper and lower outlines of the fish body. This will eliminate a weld at the nose end of the fish. (You'll undoubtedly have to add a tail, so make the weld at that end of your fish.)

After having formed all the wire pieces so that they conform to the sketch, they should now be moved to your welding table and laid out in the same form as on the sketch. They are now ready for joining. If only steel welding rod is used to construct the fish, all of the welding can be done using a steel rod. If the form is a composite of bronze and steel welding rods, however, it will be better to braze the job. This would be done using a bronze rod and flux. In either event, the welding operation can be executed with a $1/16''$ diameter welding rod.

THE 3-D ANTIQUE AUTO

In the construction of a wall hanging, you generally are concerned with only two dimensions. The earlier-mentioned antique automobile is a three-dimensional sculpture, again using welding rods. In this example, the rod employed is a bronze welding rod, since the antique look of the material blends nicely with the old car design. If you plan on painting your finished car, you will of course use steel rod.

While the antique car sculpture is three dimensional,

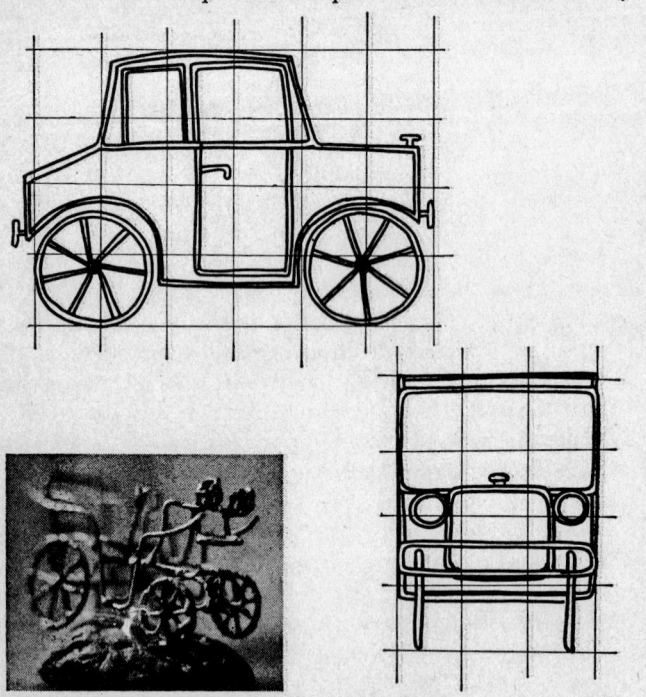

Fig. 8—Possible design for a "Tin Lizzie" drawn on a 1" grid. Wire should be formed and fitted over drawing prior to welding. Fig. 9—Another version of the antique auto, translated in wire.

it is basically a skeleton outline of the car, leaving much to the imagination of the viewer as well as the sculptor. In making an object of this type, there is no standard pattern, but, as in the case of the fish, it may be easier to sketch the car out roughly before undertaking work on the sculpture. So as to be sure that there will be some uniformity and proportions to the finished object, it might be well to do the sketching on graph paper so that again the lines of the rough sketch become a pattern to which the various pieces are bent. Since the sides of this particular piece will be the same, there will be a duplication of all the side pieces.

DEVELOPING ARTISTIC ABILITY

With these basic projects under his belt, the student sculptor-weldor can begin to undertake work which actually will reveal how much artistic talent he has. The inherent strength of properly made welded joints permits the weldor to easily construct seemingly gravity defining constructions. Any beginning sculptor feels a tinge of excitement as he finds he can easily join, to a vertical support, pieces which run parallel to the ground. Welding makes it possible, along with the important considerations of a properly weighted base and sufficiently rigid members to keep the whole thing from falling over.

It is generally a good idea to sketch, as specifically as possible, that which you wish to build. Some sculptors prefer to work spontaneously, designing as they work, but this requires a strong sense of form and a good eye for design — all of which may come in time. In your early experimentation, however, it is best to have a pre-conceived plan of attack to serve as a "roadmap" through the project.

From the simple box form, which can serve as a heavy base for some of your efforts or be incorporated into

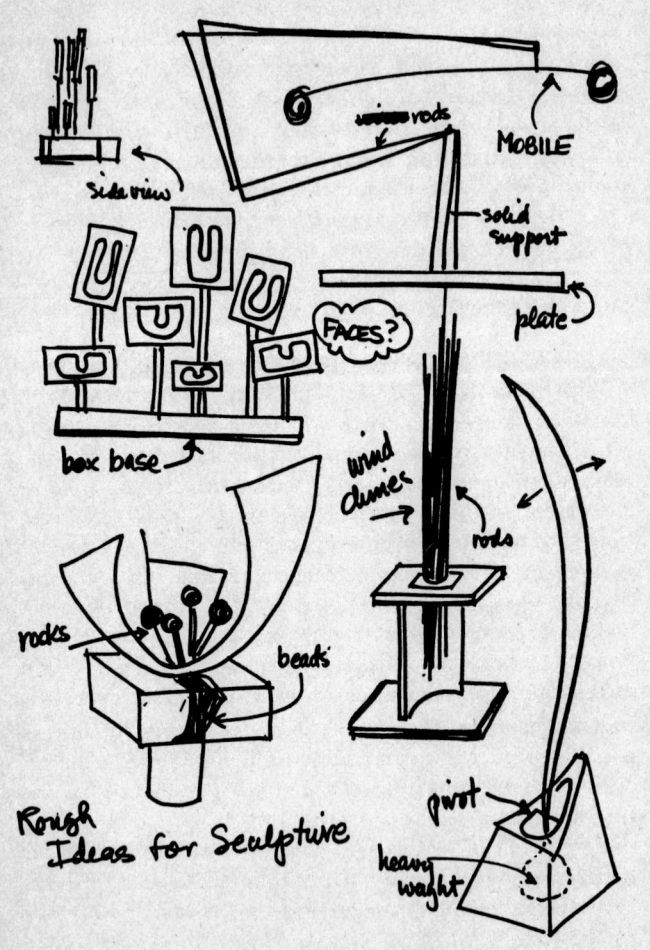

Fig. 10—The sculptor is continually on the outlook for design ideas, drawing from nature and the works of others for inspiration.

the actual sculpture, the sculptor may begin to experiment with hammered forms, metal pieces which are pounded into various shapes before joining. The surface of the sculpture offers another area for experimentation, and may be finished to add interest to the work of art. Some sculptors run beads on various surfaces; others add a bronze coating through brazing, and still others may use a combination such as sandblasting and the burning in of irregularities. While the welding of aluminum is difficult with the oxyacetylene process, that metal can be anodized (colored) following welding to give it a variety of hues. Many of these are too vivid for aesthetically-pleasing work, however, there are a number of subtle shades which metal shops specializing in anodizing will be able to produce.

Sculptors frequently, and very successfully, combine the metal of their sculpture with a number of other materials, such as rock, stone, wood, glass or plastics. Still other artists specialize entirely in "found" materials, utilizing such things as chrome bumpers from junk cars, and their eforts are artistically pleasing. For the most part, however, the amateur attempting this will end up with an amateur piece of work. As in any artistic pursuit, the serious sculptor-weldor should become familiar with what others have done, and try to duplicate some of their better efforts. The skills and the feeling for the artform acquired in this manner will help the serious sculptor-weldor develop his own style.

Lastly, a number of schools are including welded sculpture in their arts program. If you wish more professional guidance in your welding sculpturing, check with art schools or adult education programs in your area.

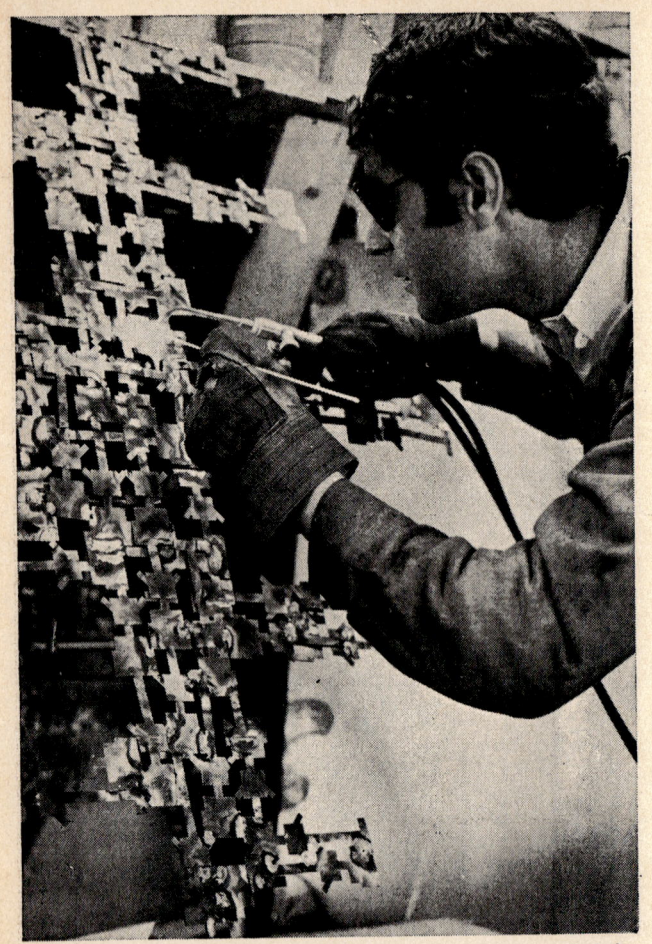

Sculptor Silas Seandel creates everything from his intricate wall design to bronze funiture bases with his welding torch.

SCULPTORS AT WORK

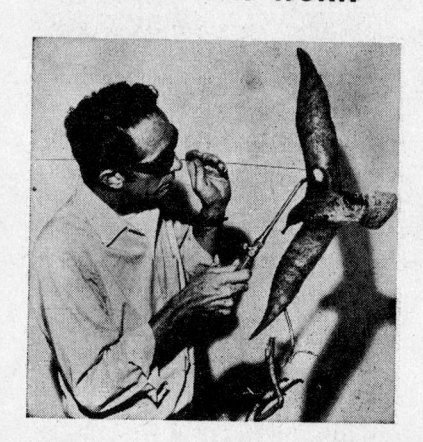

TOP—Well-known sculptor Maxwell Chayat works on an exotic sculptured candelabra.

LEFT—Laurance Burry is a self-taught West Coast sculptor who uses welding both as a vocation and hobby activity.

Frank Kawamoto's handsome eagle begins with a mandrel of welded wire, upon which additional weld metal is laid to provide a realistic appearance of feathers.

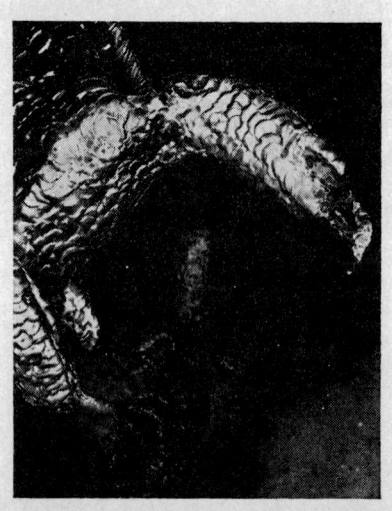

OXY-ACETYLENE WELDOR'S HANDBOOK 295

This handsome chess set even features a welded chess board. Note the detail of the whimsical chessmen shown in the photo below.

296 THE SCULPTOR WELDOR

This variety of transportation means illustrates the diversity of techniques employed in welded sculpture.

OXY-ACETYLENE WELDOR'S HANDBOOK 297

"El Toro" is made of solid bronze, through the careful manipulation of a small flame and small diameter wire. The completed work is only 3" long!

Delicate dandelions in metal grace an art show.

THE SCULPTOR WELDOR

This stainless-steel and carved stone statue stands in a San Francisco park.

ABOVE—This metal "tree" could also be used for an unusual lamp and shade.

LEFT—"Found" art can be created into artistically pleasing designs.

CHAPTER 15

WELDING SAFETY

Welding and cutting operations are relatively safe if good judgment is used in connection with such undertakings. Since many of the readers of this book will be using welding and cutting equipment outside of the normal shop areas, there are definite precautions that must be taken to avoid troublesome situations.

As has been pointed out, the oxyacetylene flame is the hottest known flame of man. A flame that is sufficiently hot to melt steel will readily burn wood, paper, rags and other combustible material that might come within its reach. In welding and cutting, that "reach" is surprisingly long.

Some of the fire hazards of these activities that are even beyond the reach of flame, inasmuch as there are times during welding and cutting operations where globules or sparks of metal fly a considerable distance from where the actual welding or cutting operations are being undertaken. Because of this, it is a requirement that combustible material be removed from the area in which this work is being done. If the room in which you're working has wooden floors, it must be protected by sheet metal. It is always advisable to have a fire extinguisher handy.

Whenever a welding and cutting operation is undertaken, remember that you are "playing with fire," but the flame is or should be under control at all times. There is little danger as long as the weldor maintains control of the flame and sees that it is not directed on combustible materials. In the chapter discussing the welding gases, you find presented safety information about the specific gases, but additional data regarding cylinder safety is given later in this chapter.

PROTECTIVE APPAREL

Often time, hobby weldors are reluctant to properly outfit themselves with protective clothing. This is a dangerous practice; there are certain items of personal apparel which should be considered as "musts". Goggles (which are discussed on page 301) are one. Gloves specifically made for weldors is another.

Weldor's gloves

Anyone doing welding or cutting should obtain a "good" pair of leather weldor's gloves. "Good" gloves are recommended because if the leather is of high quality, it will not harden under the heat of welding. Consequently, the gloves will last much longer and thus, prove to be cheaper in the long run. Leather gloves are also recommended because they are not readily combustible and resist heat. Even the most careful weldor at some time will pick up the hot end of the welding rod or a hot piece that he has been welding. When this happens, he is thankful that his gloves are leather and can protect him from a bad burn.

These gloves also should be a gauntlet type, so as to protect the wrist from both hot sparks and radiation.

Jacket

For someone doing a lot of welding, a leather jacket is a good investment. If you are just an occasional weldor, a blue denim jacket, or one made of some other tight-weave fabric which will resist sparks, will probably serve the purpose. Long sleeves are essential, and a collar which can be turned up to cover the neck will help avoid the painful "sunburn" that can be generated by the infra-red rays of the welding process.

Nylon and the other modern synthetics are not suitable for a weldor's protective clothing. While these materials may not necessarily burn readily, a hot spark can quickly "eat" right through several layers of these fabrics to the skin underneath.

Aprons and pants

Some weldors wear leather aprons, others get by with canvas aprons, but here again, this protection is recommended. Leather pants are available for weldors, but jeans or similar material are suitable. Be sure, however, that the pants have no cuffs. Anyone that welds consistently in cuffed pants soon finds that he has hot feet and no cuffs. Cuffs catch the sparks and are soon burned off. Eliminate them beforehand to avoid this hazard.

WELDING GOGGLES

No welding should be undertaken without adequate eye protection, and so goggles are an essential part of the weldor's equipment. In welding and cutting operations, the rays from the intensely heated solids or gases may be in one of three classifications:

1. Visible light rays
2. Visible ultra-violet rays
3. Invisible infra-red rays

Long ago, man learned that the sun's rays are harmful to his eyes, so he never looks directly at the unclouded sun. Radiation from welding heat sources is injurious to the eyes for exactly the same reasons, and because of the same type of radiation. Welding goggles are fitted with absorption lens which cut out a good deal of the ultra violet and infra-red radiation and remove most of these harmful rays. These lens in the goggles you select should be to National Bureau of Standards specifications, which have been assigned lens shade numbers for various types of welding operations. A minimum shade lens for light welding is a number 4; for minimal flame cutting — a

WELDING SAFETY

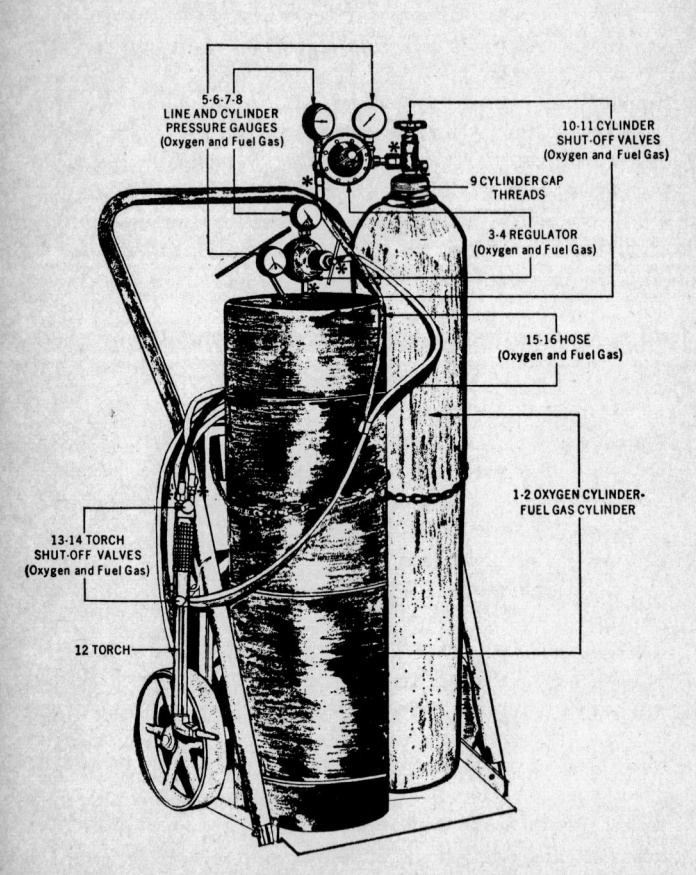

5-6-7-8 LINE AND CYLINDER PRESSURE GAUGES (Oxygen and Fuel Gas)

10-11 CYLINDER SHUT-OFF VALVES (Oxygen and Fuel Gas)

9 CYLINDER CAP THREADS

3-4 REGULATOR (Oxygen and Fuel Gas)

15-16 HOSE (Oxygen and Fuel Gas)

1-2 OXYGEN CYLINDER- FUEL GAS CYLINDER

13-14 TORCH SHUT-OFF VALVES (Oxygen and Fuel Gas)

12 TORCH

Specific safety suggestions for the numbered items are presented on the following pages.

number 5. For normal gas welding and cutting operations, a number 6 lens is recommended.

EQUIPMENT SAFETY

Oxygen cylinder (1)

Don't refer to oxygen as "air". Don't use oxygen from a cylinder without the proper pressure-reducing regulator. Don't permit welding or cutting sparks or flame to contact cylinder. Don't try to mix gases in a cylinder. Don't hammer on cylinders, or throw or bang them around. Don't use oxygen as a substitute for compressed air.

Acetylene cylinders (2)

Don't refer to acetylene as "gas". Don't use acetylene at a pressure exceeding 15 psi. Don't lay an acetylene cylinder on its side. Use only soapy water to test for acetylene leaks, never an open flame.

General cylinder safety (1-2)

Don't tamper with cylinder safety valves. Don't hang torches on cylinders or regulators. Recap the cylinder whenever gauges and regulators are removed. Never transport a cylinder without taking proper safeguards to protect against shifting or falling. Cylinders should not be allowed to stand alone without being secured with a lashing or chain, to prevent them from toppling. Never use choker slings or magnets to hoist a cylinder; also, never hook into the protective cap.

Regulators (3-4)

Inspect to be sure there are no open flames or other ignition sources in the immediate area, then "crack" the valve to blow out any dust or dirt before connecting the regulator. When setting up a rig, be sure to install a regulator in the line. Screw the regulator stem all the way out before placing pressure on the regulator. Before removing it, close the cylinder valve and vent the regulator of any residual gas.

Pressure gages (5-6-7-8)

Because the threading is different for each, the oxygen gauge will fit only the oxygen cylinder and the fuel gas gauge fits only the fuel gas cylinder. The difference in the thread sizes will prevent interchanging the connections. Observe each gauge frequently to note any trouble, such as unusal movement or jamming of the pointer. When any trouble is noted, close cylinder valve and discontinue use of the outfit until the trouble is located and corrected. Never lubricate gauges, regulators, valves or connections; lubricant can react violently with oxygen. For the same reason, don't open valves while wearing greasy gloves.

Cylinder cap threads (9)

Avoid striking or scoring the cylinder cap threads or distorting the caps; otherwise, they will not screw on properly. Never lubricate them with oil or grease.

Cylinder shut-off valves (10-11)

If you hear a leak around the stem after opening the valve, try to stop the leak by tightening the connecting nut. If you are not immediately successful, close the valve and tag the cylinder, then have the cylinder removed from service. Whenever you use a wrench to open or close a cylinder valve, be sure not to leave it on the stem where someone could accidentally strike it and release gas. The wrench should be kept close-at-hand, to be instantly available at all times in case of emergency.

Torch (12)

Before beginning work, check torches for leaks in shut-off valves, hose couplings, or tip connections. Never use a defective torch. Inspect torch tips for clogging. Clear blockage with proper cleaning tool before beginning work. Never light a torch from hot work or with matches; only use a friction lighter.

Torch shut-off valves (13-14)

Inspect frequently for leaks. Do not depend on the

valves to prevent gas leakage when torch is left unattended at the worksite for extended periods of time. Always remove torch and hose from enclosed spaces when work is interrupted or concluded. As an additional precaution, close shut-off valves on cylinders.

Hoses (15-16)

Hose, probably the most fragile part of any burning or welding system, should be inspected frequently, especially before being used. Never use a system which does not distinguish (by color or other means) between the hose carrying oxygen and the one carrying fuel gas. Couplings are designed so as not to be interchangeable — fuel gas couplings are left-hand threaded, while oxygen hose couplings are right-hand threaded. Never use a hose which carries fuel gas and oxygen simultaneously (having only a common wall construction to separate them.) Should a breakdown occur in the separation wall, the two gases could mix, with serious results. Connections which can be joined by being pushed or separated by a straight pull motion should not be used. Only couplings which require a rotary motion to be joined should be used.

Pressure test any hose which has had a flashback, or one which on inspection shows excessive wear. Fuel gas and oxygen hose which have been disconnected from the torch or other gas consuming device should be removed immediately from a confined space.

FINAL NOTES

Always remember that welding and cutting is as safe an operation as the user of the torch makes it. Extreme care must be taken at all times to see that the flame is directed on the workpiece and not on some woodwork that might be in the vicinity.

A spark from a cutting operation can travel 20 to 30 ft. from where the work is being undertaken; consequently, readily combustible materials must be kept at least that far from the work area.

The hottest flame on earth is no respecter of a person if the one using it is careless. He can be burned and his property destroyed. Use it with care.

A fire extinguisher and burn ointment can be a couple of handy accessory items for the welding area. If you abide by the safety guidelines mentioned here, their use should never be necessary.

INDEX

A
Acetone, 23, 24
Acetylene, 17, 24
  Cutting, 234
  Cylinders, 23, 303
  Feather, 64
  Flame, 64
  Generation, 18
  Generator, 20
  Storage, 24
  Withdrawal Rate, 24
Adhesion, 118
Aircraft Welding, 224
Alignment, 111, 120, 216, 221
Alloys, 153, 173, 178, 181, 184, 185, 232
Aluminum, 47, 173, 291
Apparel, Protective, 300
Aprons, 301
Asbestos, 40, 143, 163, 171
Auto, Welded Sculpture, 288

B
Backhand Welding, 78, 79
Back-up Strip, 168
Bead, 92, 182, 189
Bell Hole Welding, 218
Bend Test, 198
Beveling, 71, 99, 175, 178
Blow Hole, 125, 143
Bourdon Tube, 31
Branch Connections, 219
Brass Welding, 163
Brazing, 227
  Silver, 228
Bronze Welding, 97, 143, 146, 165
Butt Joint, 88. 92, 173, 186, 210, 216, 226

C
Carbide, 17
Carbon, 44
Carburized Weld, 127
Carburizing Flame, 64, 65, 127, 158, 167, 190, 231, 248
Cast Iron, 124, 140
  Brazing, 143, 228
  Fusion Welding, 142
  Hard Spots, 124
  Malleable, 145
  Preheating, 141
  Caulking, 89
Chipping, 156
Chromium Alloys, 157
  Molybdenum Steels, 147
Cleaning Flame, 143
Clothing, 300
Codes, 204, 247
Collar Weld, 97, 143, 165
Common Defects, 127
Cone, 64
Contraction, 101, 181, 188
Copper, 159, 278
  Alloy Welding, 163, 171
Corner Joint, 213
Corrugated Patch, 112
Coupons for Test, 196
Creep, 33
Cutting, 234
  Attachment, 235
  Cast Iron, 247
  Effect, 247
  Hints, 249
  Machine, 243
  Manual, 235
  Stack, 246
Cylinders, 10
  Acetylene, 17
  Oxygen, 10
  Storage, 16
  Safety, 16, 303

D
Defective Welds, 114, 127, 158, 165, 178
Deoxidized Copper, 161

INDEX

Design, 87, 188, 207, 214, 222,
Diaphragm, 27
Dished Patch, 112
Distortion, 142, 155, 175, 189, 221,
Double Bevels, 93, 99
  Vee, 99
  Welding, 80
Ductility, 198

E
Elasticity, 195, 198
Elbow, 95
Electrolytic Copper, 160
Elongation, 195, 198
Etching, 202
Examining, Weldors, 193
Expansion, 101
Eye Protection, 301

F
Face Bend Test, 200
Fade-away Weld, 84
Feather, Acetylene, 64
Filler Rod, 44
  Testing, 48
Fillet Weld, 90
Fish Plaque, 286
Flame Adjustment, 60, 190
  Carburizing, 64, 65
  Neutral, 64, 66
  Oxidizing, 64, 66
  Temperatures, 19
Flame Cutting, 234
  Bevel, 98
  Effect, 247
  Equipment, 235
  General Principles, 234
  Tip Selection, 252
  Variations, 251
Flange Bottom, 94
Flanged Edges, 73, 170, 175, 185
Flowers, Welded 278
Flush Weld, 91
Fluxes, 39, 157, 165, 170, 178, 186
Forehand Welding, 76, 180
Free Bend Test, 198
Freezing, 33, 74

Furnace, 43
Furniture, 267
Fusion, 117

G
Gases, 10, 41, 172
Gauges, Pressure, 31, 304
  Service,
  Weld, 123
Generator, Acetylene, 20
Gloves, 300
Goggles, 301
Grinder, Use of, 40, 182

H
Hard Facing, 204, 232
Hard Spots, 124
Headers, 220
Heat of Oxy-Acetylene Flame, 19
High Carbon Steel, 149
Horizontal Welding, 83, 172
Hose, 34, 305

I
Incipient Crack, 119
Inclusions, 117, 202
Inside Lap Weld, 94
Inspection, 114

J
Jacket, 300
Jigs, 105, 168, 177, 212, 214, 222, 226, 230
Joint Preparation, 98, 104, 141, 142, 155, 157, 166, 174, 185, 215

K
Kerf, 239
Kerosene Test, 201

L
LP Gas, 25, 41, 109, 233, 253
Laminations, 117
Lance, 251
Lap Weld, 91
Lead Welding, 171
Leaks, Locating, 24, 303
Leaves, Welded, 281
Lighters, 38
Liquid Air Process, 11
Low Alloy Steel, 153
Low Spots, 122

INDEX

M
Magnesium, 184
Malleable Iron, 145, 229
   Brazing, 227
Manganese Steel, 154
Manifolds, 15
Molds, Shape Welding, 112
Monel, 171

N
Neutral Flame, 64, 66, 177, 188, 219, 231
Nick Break Test, 200
Nickel Welding, 167
Non-rigid Joints, 102

O
Overhead Welding, 83, 180, 196, 216
Oxide, 120, 158, 177
   Films, 115, 120, 170
   Inclusions 118
Oxidized Weld, 124
Oxidizing Flame, 64, 66, 124, 169
Oxy-Acetylene Flame, 16, 64
Oxygen, 10
   Cylinder, 12, 303
   Lance, 251
   Production, 10
   Regulator, 26

P
Paddle, 180, 183
Patching, 112
Penetration, 114, 120, 148, 175
Pipe Connections, 95, 219
   Welding, 215, 217
Porosity, 118, 158, 165, 179, 200
Position of Welding, 82, 83
Preheating, 108, 141, 161, 171, 176, 182, 191
Propane, 42
Puddle Stick, 180, 183

Q
Quenching, 154, 179

R
Reducing Flame, 64, 127, 158, 188, 231, 248

Regulators, 26, 303
   Acetylene, 26
   Care of, 29
   Operation, 28
   Oxygen, 26
   Two Stage, 29
Rigid Joints, 102
Ripple Weld, 78
Rod Manipulation, 74, 80, 156, 163, 168, 170, 179, 180
Rods, Welding, 44
Rose Welded, 278

S
Safety Rules, 12, 20, 23, 251, 303-305
Sand Blasting, 40, 141
Sculpture, 275-298
Seam, 92, 94, 210
Semi-rigid Joints, 102
Setting-up Apparatus, 50, 235
Shape Welding, 112
Shear Vee Bronze Weld, 97
Sheet Metal Welding, 222
Silver Brazing, 161, 169, 171, 228
Single Bevel, 99
   Vee, 196
Slag Inclusions, 118
Soapsuds Test, 23, 201
Spark Tests, 150
Specifications for Filler Rods, 47
Square Corner Seams, 94
Stainless Clad Steel, 156
   Steel, 154
Strap Weld, 91
Successive Pools, 84
Swish Weld, 84

T
Tack Welds, 92, 148, 188, 212, 215
Tank Welding, 105, 210
Technique, Welding, 142, 147, 148, 152, 154, 155, 158, 161, 167, 179, 191
   Thin and Thick, 72, 95
   Flanger Edges, 73, 175
   Thick Sections, 95

INDEX

Technique, Welding (cont.)
   Rod Manipulation, 79, 142, 147, 148, 155, 158, 168, 188
   Double Welding, 80
Tensile Test, 5, 195
Terminology, 7-8
Test Specimens, 196, 198, 199, 219
Testing, 138, 145, 193
Torch, Classification, 35
   Cleaning, 37
   Cutting, 234
   Lighters, 38
   Preheating, 41, 109
   Welding, 34, 304
Training Operators, 130
Tulip, Welded, 281

U
Undercut, 119, 217

V
V-block, 109
Vee, 99, 175, 184, 196
Vertical Welding, 82, 181, 196

W
Weld, Carburized, 127
   Design, 87, 188, 207, 214, 222
   Oxidized, 124
   Rigid and Non-Rigid, 102
   Tests, 138
Welding Equipment, 26
Welding Fittings, 96
Welding History of, 5-6
Welding Safety, 299
Welding, World of, 1-3
White Metal, 190
Wrinkle Bending, 219
Wrought Iron, 147